MW01098299

GAY SEX

A MANUAL FOR MEN WHO LOVE MEN

by JACK HART

illustrated by BRADLEY M. LOOK

Boston • Alyson Publications, Inc.

Copyright © 1991 by Jack Hart. All rights reserved.
Illustrations copyright © 1991 by Alyson Publications, Inc.

The entry for Sexually Transmitted Diseases
is reprinted with permission from *The Alyson Almanac*.
Copyright © 1990 by Alyson Publications, Inc.

Typeset and printed in the United States of America.

Gay Sex is published as a trade paperback original by
Alyson Publications, 40 Plympton St., Boston, Mass. 02118.
Distributed in the U.K. by GMP Publishers,
P.O. Box 247, London, N17 9QR, England.

First edition, first printing: December 1991
Second printing: July 1992

ISBN 1-55583-170-2

Library of Congress catalog card number 91-58576

CONTENTS

INTRODUCTION

When my publisher first approached me about writing this book, I was skeptical. "People don't learn about sex from a book!" I protested. Besides, weren't several gay sex manuals already available? Did the world really need another one?

I was wrong on all counts.

My first error became clear a few weeks later. I was at the home of a friend, a man in his late thirties who, two years earlier, had been divorced and come out, though not quite in that order. A copy of *The Joy of Sex* was on his reading stand. I didn't understand why a man who was happily involved in a gay relationship would be reading a straight sex manual, so I inquired.

"Since I found a boyfriend a year ago, I've been discovering how much I don't know," he answered. "Ron is perfectly happy to teach me things, but I really wanted another perspective on it all. That book was the only thing I could find."

In the months since then, I've looked at several straight sex manuals. A few might have some value for gay men, but *The Joy of Sex* is not among them. Already I could see that there was a bigger need for this book than I had thought.

Next I took a field trip to A Different Light, a bookstore that seems to carry just about every gay book ever written. A conversation with one of the clerks revealed that only two gay sex manuals had ever been published. *The Joy of Gay Sex* was already long out of print, and *Men Loving Men* was about to go out of print. Both were written in the 1970s. They were good books in their day, but in a world invaded by AIDS, they had become dangerously outdated.

And so I was quickly transformed from being a skeptic about the need for this project, to a firm believer. I got to work. I thought I already knew a thing or two about gay sex, but I was surprised at how much I could still learn from other books, and from conversations with other gay men. I hope I've been successful at passing along not only some of my new knowledge, but also my conviction that in a complicated world, sex can still be a simple release of tension, a warm way of sharing, or just good fun.

If you've picked up this book, then you're interested in gay sex. Perhaps you've just started to explore your own sexuality — you're wondering if you're gay, and eager to find out what it involves. Perhaps you've been married, but you want to explore some gay feelings, and you realize that you have a lot to learn. Or you may have been enjoying sex with other men for years, and just want to know if you've been missing anything.

I tried to keep all those needs in mind while writing. I've assumed as little as possible; terms that may be unfamiliar to even a few readers are briefly defined, in parentheses, before a longer discussion begins.

Once you've left the world of kindergarten and ABC books, it's safe to assume that whenever a book is arranged alphabetically, you don't need to read the pages in order. *Gay Sex* is no exception. Look up the subjects that interest you most, then flip through it at your leisure. That can be done alone, but if you have a lover, why not browse together? I hope this book will serve as a catalyst for new activities.

Many people provided suggestions and advice as I wrote *Gay Sex*. A number of men candidly described their experiences and feelings, which I have quoted or paraphrased throughout the text. I insisted before the interviews that I would change their names, and I've done so, even for those who felt it made them appear "closeted." Guaranteed anonymity, I felt, was the best way to encourage absolute candor. Adrien Saks and Sasha Alyson read early versions of the manuscript and made many helpful suggestions, while Christopher A. Tuttle and Bill Andriette helped with specific sections.

Most of all, though, I want to thank Pat Califia. For many years I've enjoyed reading her "Advocate Adviser" column, and I was delighted that she consented to read and comment extensively on the manuscript. It is a much better book because of her insights. On some issues, however, I have disagreed with various people who read the manuscript, and opinions expressed in these pages are strictly my own.

Jack Hart
July 1991
San Francisco

GAY SEX

A

AGE DIFFERENCES. Gay people accept age differences in a relationship more readily than do heterosexuals. Many gay couples are decade or so apart in age, and the different perspectives add spice to a relationship.

A good many men over forty, however, want only much younger partners. If this description fits you and you're getting what you need, congratulations. You don't need advice.

But if you're looking for a much younger lover and find yourself frustrated by relationships that never happen, or that are consistently

short-lived, it's time to re-think your approach. We can't transform our patterns of sexual attraction at will, but neither are we totally at their mercy. Break the habit of categorizing people, the moment you meet them, as Possible Lover or Not A Possible Lover. Give yourself a chance to find out what a man is like. Soon you'll find that while physical appearance still influences you, you can also be attracted by a warm personality, a quick intelligence, a zest for life, or a wry sense of humor.

Anticipating problems: If you're convinced that you'd only be happy in a relationship with a much older or much younger man, think about the implications a bit. Ideas that seem great as fantasies don't always work out in reality. Individuals from different generations frequently clash over sexual values, incomes, career aspirations, vacation ideas, food preferences, entertainment preferences, bedtimes, and simply how they like to spend their spare time. Before you spend years of your life on a quest for something that might not actually make you happy, ask yourself a few questions. Do you already have several friends in the age group that interests you? Do you enjoy their company, their interests? Are you comfortable with them? If so, great. But if not, there's no reason to assume you'll really be happy in a long-term relationship with someone from that age group.

AGING. Your body, including your sexual functioning, changes as you age. Erections aren't as firm as when you were twenty. You'll probably need more time, and more physical stimulation, to get an erection. It'll take longer to reach orgasm, and the post-orgasm refractory period will be longer. You may start to prefer sex in the mornings, when you're rested and erections often occur spontaneously.

In most men, these changes are well under way by age thirty, but aging is a gradual process, and it may be a few years before you notice anything different.

The conventional wisdom a century ago was that if you jerked off too much when you were young, you'd run out of juice and have to cut down on sex as you got older. Today's sex educators say the opposite: The best preparation for a sexually active old age is to have lots of sex while you're younger. It's hard to find any solid medical evidence to support this, but it sure sounds good, doesn't it?

Social changes: The stereotype of a gay man is that of Dorian Gray, craving eternal youth. This isn't just a straight stereotype; if you're a gay man under thirty it's easy to observe your older counterparts and to assume that, since you wouldn't be happy living as they do, they must not be happy.

The reality is quite different. Most older gay men enjoy their lives.

Raymond Berger, who interviewed many such individuals for his book *Gay and Gray,* drew some conclusions that challenge the usual misconceptions. He found that, with age, gay men grow increasingly comfortable with their sexual identity. While gay men are less likely to have children or spouses than their heterosexual counterparts, they compensate with stronger friendship networks. And as for sex, nearly three-quarters of the older gay men that he interviewed expressed satisfaction with their sex lives.

The fact is, wisdom usually does come with age. We've all met exceptions to this rule, but in general, gay or straight, as we get older we develop a better sense of ourselves in relation to the world around us. We learn what we enjoy, and what we don't. Perhaps we never liked the bars but went anyway, at age twenty-five, because that's where everyone else was. At fifty-five, we've learned that we don't have to follow the pack, and we've met people who share our real interests. Often, we've developed a circle of friends whose company we truly enjoy. Age frequently brings a higher income and occasionally the wisdom to use it well.

Invisibility perpetuates the negative stereotypes. Older people who live with a lifelong lover, or who socialize among a small circle of friends, are less visible than those who are still looking for whatever it is that will make them happy.

Aging is painful only to those who resist the inevitable. If you want to have sex every night, you'll resent your body when it one day refuses to cooperate. It's time to develop some other interests.

There are still, of course, those who fret about the yearly onslaught of birthdays. But in a time when AIDS is ending so many lives early, it seems insufferably boorish to complain about getting older.

AIDS. (Acquired Immune Deficiency Syndrome, a disease transmitted by sex and by other routes that weakens the body's resistance to infection and frequently results in death.)

AIDS was not identified until the early 1980s. Controversy still surrounds the subject, but scientists are gradually learning more about it. Most researchers believe AIDS is caused by an agent known as the Human Immunodeficiency Virus, or HIV. In an infected person, this virus slowly reproduces until it's present throughout the body. HIV is most often transmitted through blood or semen. Other fluids (urine, saliva, or tears) could theoretically carry HIV and transmit it to another person, but in practice, such transmission doesn't seem to occur.

In the early 1980s, when AIDS was still poorly understood, individuals were deemed to either have it, or not. That distinction is still made for statistical purposes, but it's misleading. Many AIDS educators now use the term *HIV infection* rather than *AIDS*, to emphasize the continuum of conditions caused by the virus. HIV infection progresses roughly as follows:

1. *Completely asymptomatic:* Individuals who are infected with HIV but show absolutely no symptoms.

2. *Superficially asymptomatic:* Infected individuals who are affected in ways that show up on medical tests, often as a low T-cell count, but who still feel fine physically.

3. *Mildly symptomatic:* Those suffering from occasional physical symptoms such as nausea, diarrhea, or night sweats, but able to lead a largely normal life.

4. *Seriously symptomatic:* Individuals whose infection is causing serious and ongoing health problems.

5. *Full-blown AIDS:* A person is defined as having AIDS if they are HIV-positive and have been diagnosed with one of several serious disorders that are common in people with AIDS; the most common of these are pneumocystis carinii (PCP) and Kaposi's sarcoma (KS). With the improved treatments available today, some people reach this stage, but return to superficially good health. There are no documented cases yet of individuals being completely cured.

6. *Terminal AIDS:* The opportunistic diseases that attack people with AIDS often wear down their ability to fight back, until the individual is fighting off one complication after another, then several at once. This onslaught usually, but not inevitably, leads to death.

The tendency is for a person infected with HIV to progress, sometimes quickly and sometimes quite slowly, from one stage to the next. But this is only a tendency, not a firm rule, and individuals can move in both directions.

(Once a person has been diagnosed with full-blown AIDS, as defined in stage 5, they are medically considered to always have AIDS, even if their health improves substantially. This is a carry-over from the days when AIDS was less well understood, but it still has legal ramifications: Someone officially diagnosed with AIDS may have an easier time getting certain medical or legal benefits than someone in the same condition, but who hasn't been so diagnosed.)

At this time, there is no cure for AIDS and no vaccine. Some individuals *may* have a more natural resistance to the virus than others, but that's just a theory. Don't make the deadly mistake of thinking that because you've been exposed to HIV and weren't infected, you must be immune. Many people become infected only after numerous exposures, which may break down any natural resistance that is present.

If you're already infected with HIV, you have far more options than you would have ten years ago. Your local AIDS agency, or state or local health department, can direct you to the available resources.

And if you're not already infected, there's no reason you ever need to be. Take a moment to appreciate just how much peace of mind this knowledge gives you. The rest of this book tells how you can have a great sex life without giving up that peace of mind. (See also *Bodily Fluids; HIV; HIV Status; Risk Management; Safer Sex.*)

ALCOHOL. Alcohol plays a legitimate role in life. A glass of wine with dinner tastes good and is relaxing after a day at work. A drink with a new friend helps break the ice.

Alcoholism: Unfortunately, the role of alcohol in the gay community has gone far beyond this. For many years, gay bars were the only place we could go to relax, without feeling we were on enemy turf. Today, we can meet other gay men through a vast range of activities, but the influence of the bars remains. In addition, many gay people use alcohol to escape loneliness or guilt or rejection — feelings that, even in a more enlightened society, can be crushing.

According to one study conducted in the 1970s, one third of all gay people will suffer from alcoholism at some point in their lives. Alcoholics have a life expectancy two decades shorter than their non-alcoholic counterparts — in addition to the days and weeks they'll never account for because they were in a drunken stupor. They're much more likely to kill themselves, or a friend, or a stranger, while driving under the influence. They're doing permanent, and possibly fatal, damage to their liver and other organs.

What's the difference between acceptable social drinking and

Ten symptoms of alcoholism

Are you abusing alcohol? Ask yourself these questions:
- Do I miss work because of drinking?
- Do I schedule my drinking?
- Do I need a drink in the morning to get over the previous night's drinking?
- Have I ever had a memory blackout caused by drinking?
- Has drinking ever caused me to lose a job, or ruined a relationship?
- Have I ever gotten into financial difficulties because of my drinking?
- Have I ever stolen alcohol, or money to buy alcohol?
- Do I use alcohol to build up my confidence?
- Do I drink before going to a party where I know that alcohol won't be served?
- Do I drink to escape from worries or problems?

---

alcoholism? A few experts believe that any alcohol is too much. The majority believe that the average adult male can have two or three ounces of alcohol a day without threatening his health. That means two beers at lunch, *or* a couple of martinis after work, *or* a couple of glasses of wine with dinner — but not all three. The real test for alcoholism, however, is less related to amount than to dependency. Look over the accompanying list of questions to evaluate whether you've crossed that line.

Every large city, and a surprising number of smaller towns, has a gay-oriented Alcoholics Anonymous chapter. AA has a religious foundation that turns some people off, and more secular programs have formed in many areas: Rational Recovery and Secular Organization for Sobriety (SOS) are two. A call to your doctor, or to the local health department, can start you on the road to recovery. But nobody's going to make that call for you.

Alcohol and sex: Alcohol acts as an anesthetic. From a physiological point of view, even a single drink dulls your senses and reduces your enjoyment of sex. For many men, the physical effect of one or two drinks is relatively slight, however, and is made up for by the loss of inhibitions and the role of alcohol as a social lubricant. But after more than two drinks in an evening, you simply aren't going to enjoy sex as much. Most of us have seen the spectacle of the drunk who fancies himself hot for action, but simply can't get an erection.

With the arrival of AIDS, alcohol and drug use present a new danger: they can interfere with your judgment, so that you take risks you wouldn't find acceptable if you were sober.

Long-term alcoholism can eventually cause impotence. By then, however, it will have caused so many other problems that not having sex will scarcely seem important.

ALTERNATIVES TO THE BARS. "I was twenty-two before I realized there was any place to meet guys except at the bars," says James. "Somebody I met at the bar invited me to play beach volleyball the next Sunday. It was a different crowd from what I was used to, and it was easier to meet people there. About a year later, I met Jeff through that same gay volleyball group."

It's common to hear gay men wish that there were more "alternatives to the bars" for socializing. The fact is, those alternatives exist. Most of them are low-budget all-volunteer groups, however, that don't spend much money or effort reaching out to newcomers in the community. The bars have a profit motive for advertising in the local gay paper, and they have the money to do it. The gay softball league has neither.

Your city probably boasts at least one gay recreational group:

gay softball, volleyball, and bowling are most popular, followed by running, basketball, swimming, skating, and others. Invariably, such groups are just the opposite of your old high school gym class. They emphasize participation and enjoyment — not winning. As long as you bring a positive spirit, they'll welcome you regardless of your abilities. Larger cities often support several leagues for a given sport: one that's more serious and competitive, another that's strictly recreational.

Likewise, religious groups can provide both spiritual and social support. Dignity (for gay Catholics) and the gay-identified Metropolitan Community Church are the largest.

Other possibilities include political organizations and professional groups. Finally, your local AIDS group, hotline, gay newspaper, or gay bookstore may welcome volunteer help. Through any of these activities, you can meet new people while contributing to the community.

If you have an unusual hobby, you can join a national organization for gay people who share that interest. You'll undoubtedly find other members in your area. There are national gay organizations for stamp collectors, rock climbers, military veterans, and dozens of other hobbies and professions.

How do you find out about groups and activities that you'd enjoy? There's no single, comprehensive directory. Watch your local gay newspaper carefully, and ask friends. Religious, political, and community organizations are listed by city in *The Gayellow Pages*. *The Alyson Almanac* lists national organizations, which can advise you about local chapters. Both books are listed in the bibliography.

ANAL DOUCHING. See *Enema.*

ANAL INTERCOURSE. (Sexual intercourse in which a man inserts his penis into another's anus. Commonly referred to as *fucking, butt-fucking,* and by an enormous number of other slang terms.)

Anal intercourse is the act most commonly associated with gay male sex, although about a quarter of the men responding to a 1976 survey " rarely or never" engaged in it. In the AIDS era, that number has probably increased.

At the other extreme, some gay men feel they really haven't had sex if somebody didn't fuck somebody. Ted and Andrew, for example, estimate that three-quarters of their sex consists of Ted fucking Andrew. "I enjoy other things too, like jerking off together, but the orgasms I get when Ted is fucking me beat the hell out of what I get any other way," explains Andrew. "I think it's partly just the thrill of feeling my lover inside me. Also, my prostate gland seems to be positioned so that it gets massaged as he fucks me."

Ted is equally enthusiastic about the arrangement: "I like being inside Andrew. I really feel like we're becoming one person, and I get some sort of primal satisfaction from thrusting with my hips."

Condoms: Unless you can be certain of both your own HIV status and that of your partner — and, as noted in the *Risk Management* chapter, such certainty is rare — then you're taking a tremendous risk if you fuck without using a condom, commonly known as a rubber. Let's peek in (just in our imaginations, of course!) on Ted and Andrew at this point.

They've already been doing some heavy kissing and petting, and they're both pretty hard. Now Andrew reaches onto the bedside table and grabs a new condom, still wrapped in foil. He unwraps it, taking care not to nick the condom as he does so.

Many men find that a dab of lubricant inside the condom helps transmit sensation, but Ted prefers doing without, so Andrew pulls the condom over the head of Ted's cock, and slowly rolls it down. Ted's already hard — there's no point putting a rubber on a soft penis — but he gets even harder as his lover touches him. Clearly he can't wait for what's ahead.

Once the rubber is rolled on, Ted adjusts it a bit, and squeezes the air out of the reservoir tip so there'll be space for his semen. (This isn't absolutely necessary — a typical condom can hold a quart or two of water before it bursts — but it's recommended.) Ted smears a liberal squirt of KY-brand lubricant on his sheathed cock while Andrew, who's on his back now, smears some on his anal opening. They're both itching to go at this point, and their cocks are jerking with anticipation, so without further delay, Andrew pulls his legs back toward his head and guides his partner in...

In the days before AIDS, a few men liked the sensation of being fucked with little or no lubrication. That's a risky idea when you're using condoms, which are more likely to break if you aren't using adequate lubrication. Use only water-based lubricants, such as KY, Probe, or ForPlay. (See *Condom; Lubricant.*)

If it's your first time: Getting fucked often hurts the first few times, but eventually your body will learn to relax and enjoy the new sensation.

Having the right partner will make all the difference in whether or not you enjoy this new experience. Ideally, do it with someone you already know and trust, and with whom you've enjoyed other forms of sex. Should a new partner want to fuck you, let him know that this is your first time. If he doesn't seem to care, and he's simply in a hurry to get his rocks off, find some other way to accomplish that. Avoid someone who announces that he never gets fucked. Mister Macho might be fun for some purposes, but he's unlikely to show the sensitivity you'll want on this occasion.

Why does it make such a difference? You can jerk off with a boorish and self-centered partner, or even suck each other off, and be none the worse for wear. But you won't enjoy getting fucked unless you're relaxed. Your first time, you need a partner who'll help you achieve that degree of relaxation. After that, if you decide you like things a bit rougher, you can scrap these precautions.

First, you'll need to decide on a position. A side-by-side position will help you feel more in control. Straddling him, as he lies on his back, and slowly lowering yourself onto his cock, gives you even more control. But any position that you're both happy with should work out fine.

Be sure your partner helps you relax and loosen up before getting started. He should give your cock some attention with his hands or mouth, so that you're eager to keep going, then he'll insert a well-lubricated finger or two into your anus to help relax your sphincter muscle. Only then should he roll on the condom and slowly enter you with his cock.

The anal opening is quite elastic, but until you've experienced that elasticity, you'll feel some tension as your partner pushes himself in. Breathe deeply and relax. As your partner enters you, push out slightly, just as if you were having a bowel movement. This actually makes it easier for your partner to enter.

The sensation of being fucked may be so intense that, while you enjoy it, you'll lose your erection. That's not uncommon, and you'll have no trouble getting it back later.

Homework: You'll enjoy your first experience more if you've previously explored your anal area by yourself. Insert a finger (with nails short and very smooth) or small dildo and try moving it in and out. Gradually move up to several fingers or a larger dildo, until you can accommodate something the size of a cock. You'll learn to relax as you're being entered, and you'll come to anticipate the sensations that are in store for you. (See *Dildo.*) You'll also learn the angle at which your body can best accept a dildo. If you later experience pain with a partner, it may be that he's thrusting in at the wrong angle for you.

Some men like to have an enema before being fucked, to clean out the bowels. It's not necessary, but if you want one, you can buy the apparatus at a drugstore.

If it's your partner's first time: If you're fucking someone who's new to this, take it slowly. You want to help him relax. Giving him a massage may help. Telling him to relax will help. Gently massaging his anus, slowly working in a well-lubricated finger, will help. Demonstrating that you care about him will help the most.

Use your finger to relax him. Massage his prostate gland with your finger as he masturbates himself. Most likely, he has some misgivings about what's happening; give him a chance to associate anal penetration with pleasurable feelings.

When he seems ready to take you, use plenty of lubricant. Once you've started, let him indicate when he's ready for you to push deeper. If you're causing pain as you go deeper, your cock may be going in at the wrong angle, and thus hitting his rectal wall. Try a different angle. Don't force things. At best, it will simply give your partner an unpleasant experience; at worst, you could do some real physical

damage. If he's in pain, or if it's not working for any reason, you must be willing to stop.

After the head of your cock is in, give him a minute to relax and to get accustomed to this new feeling. Then gradually push deeper, but if this is his first time, don't expect to enter all the way. Again, wait a minute before you start thrusting in and out. Let him set the rhythm at first; after a few minutes, he'll be happy to surrender himself to you.

Keep the lubricant handy; you'll need more before you're done. If this is a long fuck, put on a new rubber before you reach that final stage that leads to orgasm. Condoms aren't made to last forever, and anal sex is more abrasive than vaginal sex, for which they were designed. Also have a few hand towels nearby, so you can easily clean up any mess.

When you're done, your partner may feel a slight pain as you withdraw. You can minimize it by not withdrawing too quickly, or allow him to bear down and push your cock out.

Positions: Anal intercourse lends itself to several positions. Some of the most popular ones are described here by Ted and Andrew, who seem to have tried everything at least once.

Legs up: Andrew lies on his back, with a pillow under his hips. He spreads his legs slightly and brings his knees back toward his face. Ted kneels to enter him and Andrew can rest his legs on Ted's shoulders. As Ted fucks, either of them can pump Andrew's cock.

Gay missionary: Andrew lies on his stomach, while Ted lies on top of him. Usually Andrew slips a pillow under his pelvis. This position gives Ted complete control over his rate and speed of thrust. Either of them can slip a fist under Andrew's hips and masturbate him, but not everyone likes this touch. "Having a fist under my abdomen, with the body weight of two men on top, just isn't that comfortable," explains Andrew. "I prefer to just enjoy the feeling of having Ted inside me, hearing him pant and feeling his cock stiffen just before he comes. After he pulls out, then I kneel over him and jerk off onto his chest. By that point, I'm ready to come almost instantly."

If you do expect to come while being fucked, put a towel down before you get so engrossed that you forget. Don't spoil a hot evening with an argument about who has to sleep on the wet spot.

Skygazing: Picture Ted and Andrew in the position just described. Now, without uncoupling, they roll over so that they're both looking up, and Andrew is on top. In this situation Andrew shares control of the tempo and thrusting, and his hands are free to stroke his own cock. (They can also roll just halfway, so they're both on their sides.)

Cowboy: Ted's on his back. Andrew kneels over his crotch, straddling Ted's body, and lowers himself onto Ted. This gives Andrew maximum control and freedom. They can talk, or watch each other writhe, and both can watch as Andrew shoots onto Ted's chest.

Doggie style: Andrew gets on his hands and knees, while Ted kneels and enters him from behind. "I really get turned on watching my cock pumping in and out of him," says Ted. It's also easy for him to reach forward and jerk off Andrew.

Standing: Sometimes, quickie sex must occur in cramped quarters — the broom closet at the university, for example. "We did it in the bathroom on an airplane, somewhere over Nebraska," reminisces Andrew. "It was night, and we waited until most people were asleep and there were plenty of extra bathrooms. It'd be awkward to walk out of a bathroom together and find somebody standing there, waiting to use the thing."

When space permits, the man in front often bends forward to facilitate entry. Few men actually prefer to fuck or get fucked while standing, but don't let that stop you from trying it if the urge strikes.

Afterward: A good fuck can get messy. You and your partner may both want to shower afterward. If you were fucked, and especially if you're inexperienced, you'll probably also want to sit on the toilet for a bit. This sensation is largely an illusion. Your body just got a message that it was full down there, and still wants to do something about it. But there's no need to feel uncomfortable, or take a chance. If you need to sit on the john, do it. With time, your body will learn to distinguish these false signals from the real ones.

For both partners, anal intercourse is a different experience from any other kind of sex. Like other new activities, it may take time to get used to it. But for many men, it offers physical pleasures, an increased sensitivity to one's own body, and a sense of becoming one with a partner, that give it a very special place in the sexual cornucopia.

Safety: If you're fucked by a man who is infected with HIV (the virus believed to cause AIDS), and he's not wearing a condom, the virus in his semen can easily be absorbed into your body, causing you to get AIDS. This is the most common way for the AIDS virus to be sexually transmitted.

Although he's at less risk, the man doing the fucking can also get infected if he's not wearing a condom. He can absorb HIV through small cuts or sores in his penis — even through openings too small to be seen or felt. Uncircumcised men are believed to be more prone to such infection, perhaps because the head of their penis is normally

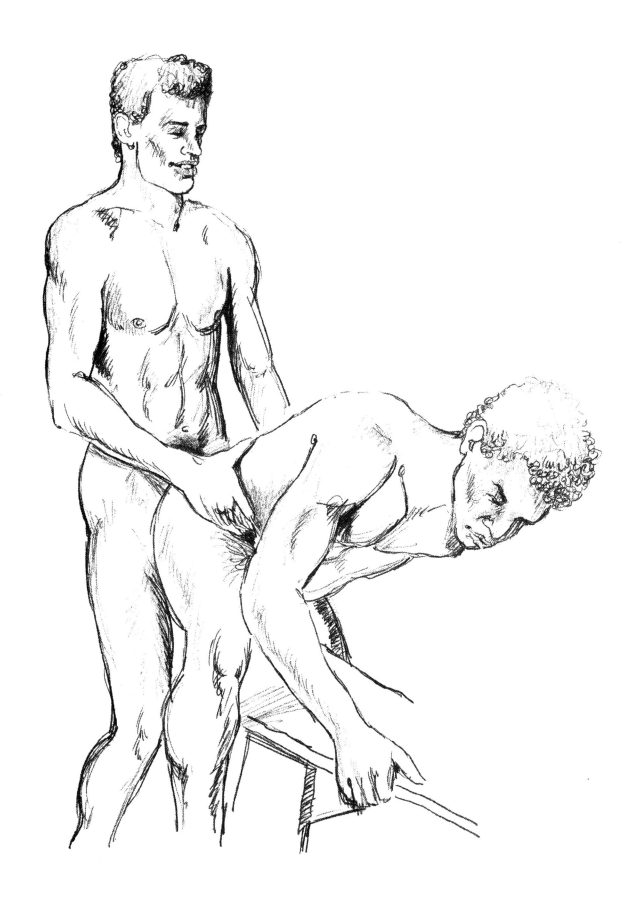

22 ❖ ANAL INTERCOURSE.

covered, and thus the skin is thinner and more easily scratched during sex.

With a condom, anal intercourse involves virtually no risk of transmitting AIDS as long as the rubber doesn't break or slip off. HIV cannot penetrate the latex barrier.

But rubbers sometimes *do* break, and they do slip off. You can minimize these dangers by following the precautions discussed under *Condom*— it's especially important to use only water-based lubricants. If you're going at it for a long time, take a breather and replace the condom; just like the rubbers you put on your feet when it's raining, prolonged friction will eventually wear out these rubbers. To reduce the likelihood of it slipping off, withdraw promptly after you come, and before you lose your erection.

As long as you're not totally wrapped up in things, you can tell if your rubber breaks. Experiment with this, so that you can recognize the sensation should it happen: Masturbate while wearing a condom, then pull away a bit of the rubber and carefully use a pair of scissors to make a small tear. Notice how it feels as the opening expands.

Should you be worried by the danger of breakage or slippage, you can further reduce the risk withdrawing before you ejaculate.

Some men think they can skip the rubber entirely if they withdraw before they come. It's not that simple. Your pre-cum — the fluid that often oozes out as you get excited — can carry HIV. And even with the best of intentions, many men, as they get increasingly close to orgasm, just don't make it out in time. If you don't believe this, ask someone who counsels pregnant teenagers.

ANILINGUS. See *Rimming.*

ANIMAL NOISES. Good communication with your partner makes for better sex. How else can he know what you're feeling, and what you want? None of us is a mind reader.

But words aren't the only way to communicate. During sex it's often easier, and more effective, to moan and gasp in ways that you wouldn't, say, at a black-tie banquet, as a way of indicating what you like. A series of moans tells your lover that you like what he's doing, more convincingly than any words could. Maybe you'll bring out the animal in your lover, as well.

ANONYMOUS SEX. (Sex enjoyed strictly for its own sake, in which the participants show no particular interest in one another's names, personalities, or interests.) See *Casual Sex.*

APHRODISIAC. (A substance considered to increase one's sex drive.)
Many foods and other substances have been reputed to act as

aphrodisiacs. Mushrooms and asparagus are often nominated for the honor because of their vaguely phallic shapes, vine-fresh tomatoes because of their odor, and ginseng on general grounds of exoticness. None will really increase your sexual potency, but they won't hurt you, either.

Not so with the famed Spanish fly. Because it irritates the urinary tract, and thus causes a slight tingling, this substance has wrongly won a reputation as an aphrodisiac. It's not; it can cause serious damage to your innards, and has even killed a few people. It's rarely found in the U.S., but you can still encounter it abroad.

Some people credit alcohol with aphrodisiacal powers. Actually, it lowers your nerve sensitivity and responsiveness, but also lowers your inhibitions. Most people enjoy sex best when they're completely sober. If inhibitions or self-consciousness interfere, a single drink may smooth the way. Beyond that, it's all downhill.

The best thing to do when you're just not in the mood for sex is not to look for an aphrodisiac, but rather go to the movies or play tennis. It's fine for an entire book to focus only on sex. It's depressing for an entire life to do so.

APPEARANCE. The world constantly bombards us with messages about the importance of looking good. We learn that it's important to be attractive, and we learn to want an attractive partner.

Likewise, social pressures influence *what* we find to be attractive. If you're turned on by blond hair, or big muscles, or youthfulness, you probably feel that's natural. It certainly *seems* natural.

But in fact, different cultures have fetishized quite different traits. Obesity and old age, considered unattractive in mainstream America, have each been found sexy in other times and places. It's our social conditioning, more than any genetic predisposition, that shapes our perception of beauty. A few remarkable people have overcome this conditioning. Most of us are still influenced by it.

Living with reality: Let's not sugar-coat the facts. If you're unattractive by conventional standards, you'll have fewer options for lovers and sex partners than someone who's strikingly handsome.

A few things about your appearance are easy to change, and you may choose to go that route. Ask your barber to suggest a new hair style. If you don't like the way you look in glasses, consider contact lenses. Start using that gym membership that you paid so much money for. Also be sure your personal hygiene is in order. Do you shower regularly? Use deodorant as needed? Do you have a breath problem? (Your dentist is the person most likely to give an honest answer to this question, and may be able to suggest corrective action, if needed.)

There's only so much you can do to physically change your appearance. As your mother probably told you, however, your personality also affects the way people perceive you. We've all met the man who's physically not that attractive, but who has such a strong and positive presence that people are drawn to him anyway. They may not fall into bed with him as readily as they do with Body Beautiful, but chances are, he gets his share of both friends and lovers.

You can't remake your personality completely. Don't even try — you'll seem phony. But if you're not happy with the way people respond to you, then give some thought to what habits you may have acquired that turn people off. Do you tend to be critical all the time? Always the pessimist? Do you perhaps exude an air of superiority, or hog the conversation?

Finding a partner: Good-looking men are no better in bed than men of average or below-average looks. That's self-evident when you think about it. But it bears emphasis because many of us, without having consciously thought about it, assume that a really cute guy will be especially hot in bed. If anything, the connection is just the opposite: Great Beauties are often lazy in bed, because they're accustomed to having the world come to them.

If you feel that nobody's interested in you as a lover or sex partner, you may just be setting your sights on too small a group. The Great Beauties of the world mostly pose and cruise other G.B.'s. The rest of us just have to make do with one another. Between you and me, I think we have more fun. (See also *Body Image.*)

B

BACKRUBS. The invitation, "Would you like a backrub?" has led college freshmen to deeper waters in dormitories around the world.

What's nice about backrubs is that they're so versatile. Sometimes they serve only their ostensible purpose: to relax the tensed back muscles after a stressful day at the office, or a tough day on the softball field. Other times, they're a conscious prelude to sex. And occasionally — as in those dormitories — they're just what's needed to break the ice. The techniques described under *Massage* are easily adapted to a simple backrub.

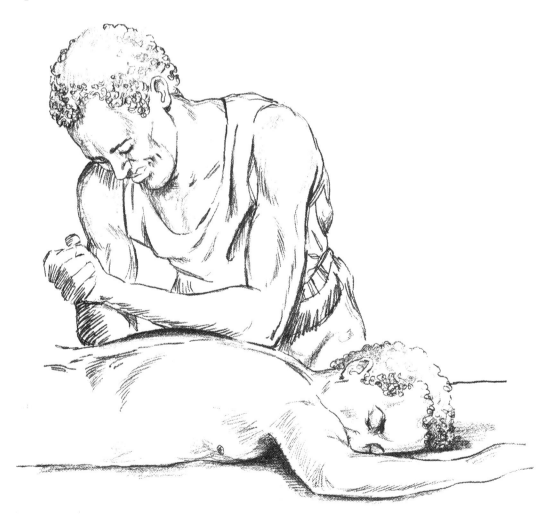

BARS. Right through the 1970s, gay bars were clearly the place to meet other gay men, to socialize, or to find a lover or sex partner. Often they were the only place.

With the growth of a gay community, there are now many alternatives. Gay bars continue to thrive, however, and they serve a useful role. When you're out of town, there's no easier place to meet other men than at the local watering hole. At home, it's still enjoyable to relax with friends at the neighborhood bar. And if you like to dance, the gay bowling league just won't fill all of your social needs.

Only in the most gay neighborhoods will the gay bars be obvious as you walk down the street. In other locales, you'll need guidance. Advertisements in the local gay newspaper are the best way to find them, or call a hotline (see *Hotline*). Gay guidebooks provide listings for gay bars throughout the U.S., and even internationally — in the U.S., *The Gayellow Pages* is comprehensive and regularly updated. (See also *Alternatives to the Bars*.)

BATHS. Even in the days of the Romans, men visited the ubiquitous bathhouses with more in mind than just getting clean. By the late 1800s, homosexual bathhouses could be found in many European cities, and soon they spread to the United States.

Here, the institution of gay baths grew rapidly after World War II, and enjoyed its heyday in the 1970s. Every large city had at least one. For uninhibited sex with no emotional attachment, you went to the baths. While sex was always the main function of the gay bathhouse, some became social hangouts as well.

The AIDS epidemic took a heavy toll on gay bathhouses. In some cities, they were closed by the local health department as a breeding ground for disease. San Francisco, for example, closed its bathhouses in 1987 following a bitter controversy. In other cities, many baths closed simply for lack of business. But some survive.

The best way to find a gay bath in your area is to check a gay guidebook, watch for ads in a gay newspaper, or simply ask someone who knows the scene.

Inside: What should you expect? You'll have a chance to check valuables at the front desk when you pay. Then, generally, you'll get a choice of a room or a locker. The rooms are small, typically about four by eight feet; they offer more privacy than a locker, but cost more. Once inside the premises you'll undress, wrap a towel around your waist, lock your room or locker, and secure the key band around your ankle or wrist. Then start wandering.

Men go to the baths for impersonal sex; this is not the place to shop for a lover. You should feel free to approach men who appeal to you. Anything you say to start a conversation will probably be taken as an expression of interest; "Care for company?" is simple, but clear. Most baths provide a coffee area, bulletin board, or some other spot that lends itself to socializing. Do not, however, start having sex with someone in a public area unless you've clearly seen that this is the custom. Orgy rooms were once common in bathhouses; today they're the exception.

Some men will have sex with several partners during the course of the evening. If the man you're with doesn't seem interested in reaching orgasm, don't take it personally. He's probably just trying to stay fresh enough to handle a few more encounters before he heads home.

Because sex in the baths is so free of any sense of obligation or commitment, many patrons will readily have sex with someone they might not choose to see on a long-term basis. As long as you have that same flexibility, you should have no trouble finding partners.

Many baths have rules forbidding unsafe sex; enforcement varies considerably. Despite their reputations as a mecca for high-risk sex, it's every bit as possible to have safe sex in the baths as in your bedroom. The temptations to do otherwise may be stronger in a bath, but it's easy to walk away if your potential partner just doesn't share your concerns. (See also *Casual Sex.*)

BATHTUBS. Assuming you and your partner aren't too big, and your tub isn't too small, a shared bath can provide a relaxing prelude to an evening in bed. Fill the tub with the warmest water you can stand. If possible, plug up the overflow drain so that when you get in, the water can rise almost to the top. Most tubs are too small to easily face each other. It's more comfortable for the taller man to sit in back; then the shorter one sits between his legs.

Turn up the heat slightly so you won't be chilled afterward, and plan what you'll need so you won't have to get out of the tub. Scented bath oils? Bubble bath? Candles? Champagne? Warm towels? Robes to wear while you go from bath to bedroom?

A few lucky people have a hot tub in their backyard. It offers all the pleasures of a bathtub, plus you can invite guests.

BEACHES. Most large beaches have a gay section, but only in gay resort areas is that section immediately obvious. In resorts like Provincetown, for example, half the beach is gay, and it's pretty hard to miss.

But at spots where heterosexuals are in the majority, you'll walk at least fifteen minutes from the parking lot, and in rare cases as much as an hour, to get to the gay area. The whole point is to be far enough from the regular flow of beach traffic to have some privacy. This isn't because everybody's having sex on the gay beach — they aren't — but

merely to allow a live-and-let-live atmosphere without confronting teenage boys eager to demonstrate their machismo.

Gay men at the beach will tend to be younger, and often better built, than average. Some come just to show off how they look in their new swimsuits. Others are there to socialize, or for casual sports — beach volleyball is especially popular. Some are looking for sex, which usually takes place not on the beach, but in a secluded area of trees or shrubbery. (See also *Cruising*.)

BEDS. Chances are, you're stuck with your present bed until you move or redecorate. But when that time comes, give some thought to getting a bed that's good for both sleeping, and for sex.

A mattress so soft that you sink into it isn't very good for sex. Most people also sleep better, once they're used to it, on a firmer mattress. That means very firm box springs, or (better) just a mattress, sheet of foam, or futon on the floor or on an elevated platform.

If your bed is elevated, having it at groin height will make it easier to add some new positions to your sexual repertoire.

Have some extra pillows or firm cushions available. They're helpful under the hips, when fucking, and sometimes in other positions.

The area around the bed also needs attention. Ideally, you'll have a dresser within reach, so that lubricants, towels, and other items are handy, yet out of the way when they're not needed. You'll want some thin curtains or blinds, so that you can have privacy while still allowing ambient light to get in, but you'll also want thicker drapes for the occasions when you want complete darkness. Candles are most romantic when they aren't competing with outside light. (See also *Sleeping Together*.)

BESTIALITY. See *Zoophilia*.

BISEXUALITY. (The capacity for being attracted to individuals of either sex.) Several factors make life difficult for bisexuals. First, of course, bisexuals are rejected by many heterosexuals who are threatened by any non-traditional sexuality.

Second, they're often snubbed within the gay community. Many gay people went through a transitional period of identifying as bisexual, before becoming comfortable with their homosexuality. Some now assume — wrongly — that all bisexuals are simply going through a similar stage. That can lead to a patronizing attitude.

AIDS has created a third obstacle: Bisexual men are accused of spreading AIDS from the gay ghetto to the "mainstream" heterosexual world. The fact is, straight people can get AIDS from many practices, both sexual and non-sexual. Better education about AIDS and safer sex is the only real solution to this. Stigmatizing bisexuals actually makes the problem worse, as it encourages people to lie about whether they're at risk for HIV infection.

This bi-phobia (as it has been called) hurts everyone, not just bisexuals. The gay movement has created a better climate for gay people who are coming out. But some gay people now have such a strong investment in their gay identity that it discourages them from recognizing a potential for bisexuality. Furthermore, gay-identified people who do end up in relationships with the opposite sex may feel uncomfortable about revealing that fact to their peers. One prominent gay male activist spent most of the 1980s in a secretive relationship with a woman — a fact which to this day is known to only to a small circle of his friends.

Fortunately, as we enter the 1990s, the notion that the world divides neatly into gay and straight seems to be rejected more and more — especially by a new generation of activists. Let's hope that trend continues.

Bisexuals and AIDS: Bisexual men have been unfairly stigmatized for carrying HIV from the gay into the straight world. Like so many hysterical reactions to AIDS, the resulting prejudice attacks groups, when it is unsafe practices and behaviors that we should single out if we really want to stop AIDS.

AIDS has created other dilemmas for bisexual men. The most common is that of the married man who has had unsafe gay sex over the years, without telling his wife. Now he must either risk infecting her, or explain to her why he wants to wear a condom during sex. It's easy to see which is the right choice, but sitting down with a spouse for a discussion of this sort is difficult.

If you're having sex with both men and women, you have an obligation to let your partners know the score. Even if you're engaging only in safer sex with other men, that term has different definitions. Your female partners have the right to make their own decisions about what level of risk they choose to accept.

BLINDFOLD. S/M enthusiasts often incorporate blindfolds or hoods into their routines, but the experience of being blindfolded can be enjoyed by a far wider group than that. Being massaged while both you and your partner are naked, and you're blindfolded, differs greatly from the same experience without a blindfold. So does sex.

Put some thought into what you use. A strip torn from an old sheet makes a perfectly serviceable blindfold, but a black silk scarf is far more tantalizing. (See also *Sadomasochism.*)

BLUE BALLS. (Testicles suffering from discomfort or slight pain, following unrelieved sexual excitement.)

Blue balls have long been a welcomed curse for straight teenage boys. They really can hurt. Yet they also provide an excuse for the line, "At this point, if you don't let me, I'll be in agony all night." What teenage girl knows enough about male physiology to argue?

Blue balls only occur after a fairly long period of excitement, and not even always in that case. Our teenager could have nipped them in the bud by running to the bathroom earlier and masturbating, had a little discomfort been his only concern.

Masturbation will relieve even a bad case of blue balls; so will time. Fortunately, there's no indication that they cause any harm.

BODILY FLUIDS. As AIDS crept into the headlines, writers and editors popularized the phrase "the exchange of bodily fluids" when discussing how AIDS was transmitted.

I wonder how many people died because these editors were afraid to use the word *semen.* Their euphemism was understood only by those who already knew what they were so feebly attempting to say.

What they were trying to say, as most of us eventually found out, was not to let another person's blood, semen (come), urine, pre-ejaculate (pre-come), vaginal fluid, saliva, or tears get into your body through any of your various body openings. If somebody's fucking you, make sure he wears a rubber, so his pre-come and come don't end up inside you. If you're sucking him off, don't let him come in your mouth.

In reality, even this more detailed warning was misleading. Most bodily fluids don't present any real danger. The vast majority of AIDS cases were (and still are) transmitted in one of four ways:

(1) via semen (or possibly pre-ejaculate), through anal or vaginal intercourse without a condom;

(2) via blood, when IV drug users share needles;

(3) via blood, through transfusions that took place before today's improved blood tests were used;

(4) via blood, as a pregnant woman passes it on to her fetus.

Other so-called "bodily fluids" — saliva, tears, and urine — carry a theoretical risk of transmitting AIDS, but in reality, the concentrations and exposures involved seem to be too small for them to pose a real threat. Most experts, for example, consider "deep kissing," in which you and a partner are exposed to one another's saliva, to involve little or no risk. (See also *AIDS; Risk Management; Safer Sex.*)

BODY IMAGE AND APPEARANCE. "One of the greatest shocks of my life," recalls Jeff, "came when I finally got to know James, who I'd been ogling over for ages, and I learned that he honestly thought he was unattractive. He didn't really blossom until after his teens, and he still carried around a lousy self-image from high school."

Body image is a tricky subject. James came across as attractive despite a poor image of himself, but often a bad self-image becomes self-fulfilling. If you're convinced that no one thinks you're attractive, it can show in your expression, your posture, your grooming, and your behavior.

Changing your self-image: What can you do if you feel you're unattractive? There are some simple steps you can take to change your looks — see *Appearance*. But don't stop there. Start keeping a written list of your best physical traits. Write down everything that you like about the way you look, and everything that other people have complimented. Add to the list when you get a chance, and read it over frequently. This sounds hokey, but it works. We all have some good physical traits and some weaker ones. Much of your self-image is determined merely by which ones you think about most. That written list will help you focus on the glass being half-full, not half-empty.

It may help to realize that virtually any physical trait will be admired by some people and disliked by others. No, that doesn't mean they're all equal. A lot of people are turned on by big chests; only a few are turned on by big stomachs. But with some ten million gay men in the U.S., some are bound to be attracted by whatever you have to offer.

Overdoing it: Oddly enough, too strong a self-image can lead to ego problems, as well. Jeff explains that "part of what attracted me to James was his shyness. I've slept with guys who thought they were Body Beautiful, and several of them expected me to do all the work. James, on the other hand, was a real tiger when we finally got together."

There's some bad news in store for those Body Beautifuls. Check out Marlon Brando in *A Streetcar Named Desire.* Now look at more recent photos of him. Yes, even Bodies Beautiful eventually fade. If you've been coasting along on just your looks, start honing your personal skills now, while you've still got some backup.

By the way, Jeff reports with a smile that James's self-image is stronger now, after two years of being bombarded with Jeff's compliments, "but it hasn't gone to his head too much. He's still a tiger in bed."

BONDAGE. (The restraint of one partner by means of rope, handcuffs, or other devices.)

Why is the fantasy of bondage so widespread? Is it all the movies we watched as kids, where the handsome hero was tied up? Maybe. More likely it has to do with the unique dynamics of control and trust, of power and helplessness.

The mechanics: Any number of bondage methods are available to you. Rope is the most common, and clothesline rope is perfect. It's soft and bulky enough not to accidentally cut into the skin, and if you don't pull the knots too tight, they'll come out easily. Several shorter ropes (about ten feet each) are more convenient than one long one. Certain items of clothing can be used instead: neckties and scarves are especially popular. Don't use anything that you aren't willing to cut apart if the knots get stuck. Jeff and James occasionally engage in light bondage scenes using Velcro tape, which is easy to secure snugly but can be quickly ripped open.

More elaborate gear is available in a well-stocked sex shop or leather shop, or from some mail-order firms. Some of it is useless. Experiment before you spend much money; once you know what you enjoy, you'll be better able to evaluate the gear that's available.

For beginners, the best equipment to buy is a set of padded leather restraints for the ankles and wrists. Attaching a rope to these, rather than tieing it directly to the body, reduces the possibility of nerve damage from getting the knots too tight. It also looks more dramatic. Chains, handcuffs, and other metal apparatus are also available, but are best left until you have more experience. These items are all painful if your weight falls on them, and embarrassing if you lose the key.

The classic position is to be tied spread-eagled on a four-poster bed, with your partner hovering over you. Few of us own four-poster beds; fortunately, there are lots of options, both prone and standing. Experimenting with them is part of the fun.

You can use just about any knot; get a Boy Scout manual if your skills are rusty in this area. (No, it doesn't have a section covering this specific situation. That's what your imagination is for.) You'll soon learn which knots come apart easily, and which don't. Bondage aficionados take special care to tie their partner in a way that is both erotic and aesthetically pleasing. They'll use more rope and knots than are really required, to create an eye-catching interplay of flesh and rope patterns.

Gags: Some couples use mouth gags in combination with bondage. But don't do it if you're new at this. While you're still experimenting, one of you may at some point really need to say something.

A clean, bulky, lint-free cloth, wrapped around the mouth several times, is the best gag. Don't put objects into your partner's mouth to gag him — they could inhibit his breathing or choke him. Adhesive tape seems like a good gag only until you take it off.

A gag should allow your partner to still make some noise. That's fine. You want to know that he's having fun, don't you? You should also agree on a way for him to signal, in an emergency, that he wants the gag quickly removed.

Bondage sex: If you tied the knots, it's now up to you to keep things going. Often you'll want to slowly masturbate your friend, letting him intensify the feelings by straining against his bonds. Being brought to orgasm while you're helpless to intervene is a very different experience from being jerked off by a partner when you're untied.

Meanwhile, you can be jerking yourself off. Or you can roll on a condom and fuck him, or have him suck you off. You can, by prior agreement, combine bondage with role-playing.

In all of this, of course, you are in control, but you have your partner's trust. It's your responsibility not to force him into an activity he really doesn't want to do. If you're into heavy role-playing, the use of a pre-designated word will let you distinguish the real *Stop!* from the just-pretend *Stop!* It's also your responsibility to be sure he isn't hurt.

Untie him soon after he comes. He's not likely to enjoy being tied up any longer, and his muscles are undoubtedly ready for a change of position.

Safety: Common sense about what you do, and who you do it with, should keep you out of most unpleasant situations. Once you're tied up, you're fully at the mercy of the man you're with. Most of us would like to know someone before we extend that much trust to him.

The safest policy is to never wrap anything around the neck, for any reason. If you decide to use a neck restraint, be sure it can be released instantly should the person pass out. (See *Strangulation.*) No restrained person should be left alone; this is especially critical if anything is around their neck.

Don't hang people by their wrists or ankles, so their body is off the floor. These joints weren't designed to take that much weight.

Have a sharp knife somewhere in the house, just in case you can't get the knots out. Better yet, have bandage scissors handy; the blunt blade goes close to the body when cutting a restraint in a tight situation. Should it come to that, cut the rope at a point as far from his body as possible. This seems self-evident now, but if your lover is suffering painful cramps and you're eager to get him free, it's easy to get careless.

If you're using handcuffs or locks, a giant key-ring looks dramatic and will make it nearly impossible to lose the key. Be especially careful with handcuffs. The cheap ones jam easily, and even the expensive ones are easy to get too tight. If you pinch a nerve with overly tight handcuffs, then can't find the key, you'll do some real damage.

Some of this advice can be ignored by experienced partners who know just how far they can go. While you're new to this, you can have plenty of excitement while staying within these guidelines. (See also *S/M; Safeword.*)

BOOKSTORES, GAY. Okay, it's a surprise to find *Bookstores* here, sandwiched between *Bondage* and *Casual Sex.* But depending on your particular bent, this listing could be more useful than either of those.

This manual attempts to give a comprehensive look at gay sex. But many subjects can be touched on only briefly here. If bondage does interest you, the nearest gay bookstore can provide books that go into much more depth about it. And there's at least one book about finding casual sex.

If you're just coming out, you have a tremendous benefit over the previous generation. Millions of other men have walked down the same path that you're on, and many of them wanted to make it easier for those who followed. They've written books about every possible aspect of being gay. You'll find some of these books in a good general bookstore. But for a really wide selection — and some knowledgeable, free advice about which books are the best — you should discover the nearest gay bookstore. They'll have novels, and collections of short stories, and non-fiction on a wide range of gay-related subjects. They'll have short, easy-to-read books about interesting aspects of gay culture, and long scholarly tomes. They'll have literary magazines, as well as erotic magazines. Oh, they're also a good place to meet men.

Porn stores: There are also adult bookstores that specialize in sexually explicit books and magazines. Most carry both gay and heterosexual material; some offer peep shows and booths in the back, where men can meet for anonymous sex.

While these stores may serve a useful function, they don't offer nearly the range of material that a general gay bookstore has. The staff will probably be far friendlier and more ordinary than the typical New-Right preacher would have you think, but they probably can't answer your questions about the gay community as well as one of the general gay bookstores described above.

C

CASUAL SEX. (Sex that takes place with no expectation of an ongoing relationship.)

Many gay men, at some period in their lives, engage in casual sex. For men just coming out, it's often a way of becoming comfortable with their bodies and their gay identity. Frequently these encounters consist of just one-night stands, or a few successive nights together, often with a great deal of shared warmth and communication, after which the two partners go their separate ways. A majority of gay men eventually come to prefer a longer-term relationship.

Casual sex differs from *anonymous sex* (or *impersonal sex*), in which the participants are quite frank that they're interested in one another only for sex. Such encounters involve little or no verbal communication or sense of intimacy.

Both casual and anonymous sex are accepted within the gay male community as valid forms of sexual behavior, though not enjoyed by everyone.

Safety: In the early 1980s, researchers noticed that most people with AIDS had engaged in sex with a great many partners, and they hypothesized that promiscuity caused AIDS. We now realize that the connection is not so simple. Men with numerous partners simply had more opportunities to be exposed to AIDS, but safer sex — not fewer partners — is the most important consideration in reducing the risk of AIDS. (See also *Baths; One-Night Stand.*)

CELIBACY. (Abstaining from sex. Except when used in a religious context, celibacy usually precludes only sex with a partner, not masturbation.)

A minority of gay men have always chosen the route of celibacy; often their reason is that a preoccupation with sex was making them miss out on too many other things that life has to offer. For most, celibacy is temporary, not a lifelong, calling.

With the spread of AIDS, this small group has been joined by men who become celibate out of fear. There's no need for this AIDS-induced celibacy, since you can have safe sex with a partner. But if the stress involved in sex robs it of any pleasure, then celibacy may be a good short-term option for someone still working through their fears.

Relatively few men remain celibate for more than a year or two, but that makes the option no less legitimate for those who do choose it.

CIRCUMCISION. (The practice of cutting off the loose skin — the foreskin — that covers the tip of the penis.)

Circumcision was practiced as far back as ancient Egypt, where it apparently served as a puberty rite to expose the male glans. Many other cultures also adopted the practice, but it's never been universal.

Until well into the twentieth century, most American men were not circumcised except for religious reasons.

Notions of male hygiene changed during World War II, and nearly all boys born during the subsequent baby boom in the U.S. were circumcised. The pendulum is swinging back now, as many parents decide to skip the operation on their newborn son, leaving him the option to have it done later if he so desires. In much of the world, including most of Europe, circumcision is uncommon.

Circumcision can be performed on an adult who, for reasons of appearance, religion, or comfort, wants it. It's a minor operation, but the recovery period involves going several weeks without getting an erection.

Rarely, however, is there a medical need for adult circumcision. Occasionally the operation is performed on a man who finds that a very tight foreskin causes discomfort during sex, but usually the owner, or a doctor, can relieve the problem by stretching the foreskin.

Men who are circumcised in adulthood disagree as to whether they enjoy sex more or less, or even whether it feels much different.

Getting it back: A few men have had the reverse procedure — creating a foreskin to replace the one that was removed in infancy — but it's more complicated. No new skin is added in this operation. Skin that's already present is merely stretched. It takes a long time, and the result won't be the same as a natural foreskin. (See also *Foreskin.*)

CLOTHING. Good sex usually starts with both of you being nude. But from that starting point, it may be enjoyable to add certain items of clothing.

Exactly what to add is a matter of individual taste. Just like discovering your tastes in food, you won't be sure until you try something. Fortunately, experimentation is easy. If that sequined jockstrap that looked so good in the catalog doesn't do anything for your lover, you can just take it off.

Certain items are sexy to a great many gay men. Jockstraps, lycra tights or bicycle shorts, swimsuits, and various types of underwear all have large fandoms. These items, of course, soon have to come off if they accomplish their goal.

Other pieces of clothing can stay on throughout your lovemaking. Some men are turned on by the sight of white athletic socks on a partner; maybe it reminds them of the basketball player who was their college roommate. A silk robe, left open in front, combines a sensual physical feeling with a sense of exhibitionism. Leather armbands, headbands, scarves, and wet t-shirts (in warm weather, only!) can all add new spice. (See also *Fetishes; Jewelry.*)

COCK RING. (A device that is wrapped around the base of the penis and scrotum to intensify an erection.)

The best cock rings are made of leather, cloth, or other flexible material. Snaps allow you to adjust the size as you secure them. Occasionally a ring is used only around the base of the penis, but with less effect.

Just as promised, cock rings do prolong an erection and make it harder. An erection is caused when the flow of blood from the penis is restricted, and a cock ring restricts it further. (See *Erection.*) Whether you like this particular feeling is a personal matter.

A solid ring of metal, plastic, or rubber can also serve as a cock ring. These are fine too, but must be carefully fitted. A metal ring that's

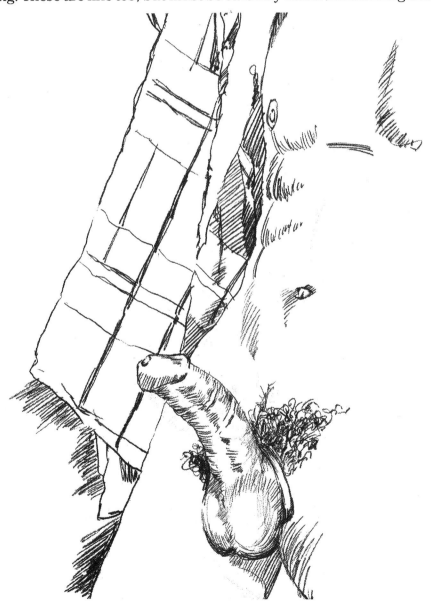

too small, set in place while you're soft, can become impossible to remove after you're hard. Since a tight ring keeps you hard indefinitely, your only alternatives at that point are a trip to the emergency room, or trying to cut the thing off yourself. Neither one will be fun.

Safety: As long as you avoid one that's too tight, a cock ring should present no safety or health problems. Some men enjoy the feel of wearing a cock ring all day, under their street clothes. That's fine, but don't wear one so tight that it causes any discomfort; remove it at night, in case your circulation was slightly cut off. And if you're wearing a metal cock ring, take it off before you go through an airport metal detector. Unless, of course, you're looking for some special attention...

COCK TEASE. Sooner or later, you'll meet a man who flirts with you, and seems eager to become intimate, but who backs off whenever you start to respond. You've met a cock tease.

Some men do this unwittingly. They only mean to be friendly, but in their zeal to be liked, they send out signals stronger than they intend. They're either inexperienced or slow-witted, and in either case, should be forgiven.

Deliberate cock teases are really being cruel, even if their cruelty is caused by insecurity. Keep your distance until they grow up.

If you feel you attract cock teases, it may be that you have a tendency to misinterpret behavior that really is mere friendliness. Don't be such an eager beaver. You need friends in life as well as lovers.

COME. (To have an orgasm; also, used as a noun, semen.) See *Ejaculation; Semen.*

COMING ON TOO STRONG. All of us have done it at least once. We decide on the first or second date that *This Is It,* and next thing you know, we've blurted out something like "I love you," or we've started talking about where to live when we both retire, and suddenly Mr. Wonderful is backing off.

Most of us have been in Mr. Wonderful's shoes, as well.

It's fine to be enthusiastic about the man you've just started dating. If you're not excited about him now, the prospects are grim for the road ahead.

But recognize that this initial enthusiasm has little to do with true, long-term compatibility. What you're feeling now is just good personal chemistry. Don't be so desperate for a relationship that you declare your undying love for the first person who seems likely to reciprocate.

You'll avoid some awkward moments if you take things more slowly. Instead of "I love you," tell him, "I think you're pretty special."

If he gives you no encouragement, repeat the same comment a few days later. If you still draw a blank, it's time to recognize that this relationship is more one-sided than you hoped.

Meanwhile, there's that dilemma on the other side of the fence: How do you fill the awkward silence after your newfound friend blurts out "I love you," and it's too early to truthfully give the response he wants? For both your sakes, don't lie. The best answer, if it's honest, is along the lines of, "That's great. I'm not sure I know you well enough to say that right now, but I'm looking forward to getting to know you better." Anything more subtle than that is likely to be misunderstood.

COMING OUT. (The process of acknowledging to yourself, or to others, that you are gay.)

Most men come out gradually. They begin by realizing that they can be attracted to other men; for a time, they may identify as bisexual. Eventually, the threatening aspects of being gay seem less dire, and the appeal of being true to their inner self grows stronger. A sexual experience or relationship with another man will often speed up the process. Only after this point do most men come out to straight friends and family.

Coming out tends to be an irreversible process. Once you've told friends that you're gay, it's hard to convince them that you were just joking, should their reaction be more hostile than you anticipated. Most men, on coming out, find that straight friends are more supportive than they had anticipated. Says 45-year-old Phillip: "The first two responses I got when I came out to two friends were, 'We've known that for ages; we always felt sorry that you felt you needed to hide it,' and 'I thought so, but I didn't want to pry.'"

Family members are less predictable, but in the long run will usually do their best to be supportive. Parents, especially, tend to feel this is a problem for which blame needs to be assigned, and often point the finger at themselves or each other. Don't let their guilt be reflected back onto you! It's good to be sure you're comfortable with yourself before coming out to parents, and have some supportive friends available, so that you can more easily find the patience to bear with them as they work through something for which their background really never prepared them.

At work: Use caution if you decide to come out at work. That means don't tell even one person without giving it serious thought; office gossip is a powerful force.

In most places, you can still be fired for being gay. Even if state, local, or company regulations forbid such discrimination, a supervisor who wants to be rid of you can find another reason, or can make life so unpleasant that you resign of your own accord.

Homophobia will only end when most people know several individuals who are gay, and anyone who comes out at work is making a tremendous contribution in that direction. But before you do it, talk to gay friends about your plans, and get a sense of both the written and unwritten policies at your workplace. You may bravely decide to come out even if you expect complications, but at least you can plan for them. Coming out just after you receive a good evaluation, for example, will make it harder for the company to turn around and fire you for an unrelated reason.

Finding and providing support: A number of books can help in your coming-out process. Any good gay bookstore or mail-order service will have a wide selection. They'll range from advice manuals to collections of coming-out stories. It's helpful merely to know that you're not the first to travel over this often rocky path. If a religious background interferes with your self-acceptance, you'll also find books documenting how respected people of many religious backgrounds — from Catholicism to Christian Science — have successfully reconciled their religion and their homosexuality. No book, however, will be as valuable as a good friend who's been through it all himself.

If you're just coming out, you'll probably end up in bed with some men who have been out for years. Don't try to hide your lack of experience. You won't succeed, and you'll lose the opportunity to learn whatever your partner could teach you.

If you're more experienced, but are having sex with a man who is just coming out, remember that this encounter may be far more intense for him than it is for you. Give him a chance to try new things and to learn more about his sexuality, but respect his boundaries, be they physical or mental.

COMPUTER SEX. As it gets easier to link your computer to others by means of a telephone line, gay men have quickly taken advantage of the new opportunities. A number of small, not-for-profit gay computer sex services have sprung up. Some offer a chance to "talk" dirty; others are mainly a way to make initial contact.

Enjoy these, if you have the hardware and inclination, but be wary about how much information you give out; there's no way to tell who's listening. Stick with a pseudonym while using the service, and if you decide to meet someone in person, do it in a public place. *Never suggest that you possess or want to buy child pornography, or are interested in sex with minors, even light-heartedly.* Law enforcement officials often monitor computer bulletin board services, and they've entrapped users on charges like these. The anonymity that makes these services so appealing makes it impossible to know that you're compu-chatting with an undercover cop.

The best way to find a computer sex line is to track down one of the many gay computer bulletin boards, then ask other users what's available. (See also *Telephone Sex.*)

CONDOM. (A thin sheath, usually made of latex, that covers the erect penis to contain semen after ejaculation. Also known as a *prophylactic* or *rubber.*)

The earliest known condom was invented in the sixteenth century by the Italian scientist Fallopius. It consisted of a small linen covering for the head of the penis, and was held in place by the foreskin of the uncircumcised user — circumcised men were just out of luck. Fallopius's device was intended merely to stop the spread of venereal disease. Two centuries later, an unknown inventor devised a way to make a condom from sheep intestines, which would cover the full length of the erect penis, thus creating a condom that could be used for birth control as well as for disease control.

Finally, with technological improvements, the modern-day latex condom evolved. Even in pre-AIDS days, gay men occasionally used condoms for disease prevention, or simply as a fetish item. Today, because they block transmission of HIV during intercourse, they're widely used and accepted among gay men.

Usage: Condoms are readily available in drugstores, and often in gay bookstores and from other gay businesses.

If you haven't used a condom with a partner, masturbate with one by yourself first, to get the feel of it. Have some lubricant handy. (Right now, it doesn't matter what kind of lubrication you use, but for penetrative sex with a partner, use only water-based brands.)

Get undressed and think about how much better this is than the last homework assignment you had. When you've got an erection, unwrap the cellophane packet around the condom, taking care not to rip the condom itself.

Dab some lubricant on the end of your cock. Later, you may decide you prefer to do without this, but most men like the sensation it provides. Put the condom on the tip of your cock, and unroll it along your shaft. Now do whatever feels good.

You'll quickly find that the rubber changes the feel of your hand as it slides up and down your cock. Many men report that it decreases sensation and helps them prolong intercourse. Previously, your body had learned to associate a slightly different stimulation with the reward of orgasm. As you learn that this new stimulation can produce an equally pleasant result, you'll find that the condom seems to transmit sensation better than it used to. But don't expect that change to happen instantly.

With a partner: The procedures with a partner are just the same. Be sure you're using a water-based lubricant such as KY, Aloe-9, or ForPlay. (See *Lubricants.*) A bottle with a spray attachment, like those used for misting plants, filled with warm water and set by the bed will allow you to quickly refreshen the lubricant as it dries out. Or you can just squirt on some more lube.

If you find that the condom cuts down on sensation for you, you may want to rely on masturbation to get your juices flowing, then roll on the condom when you're well primed.

When you're done, pull or roll the condom off and throw it in the

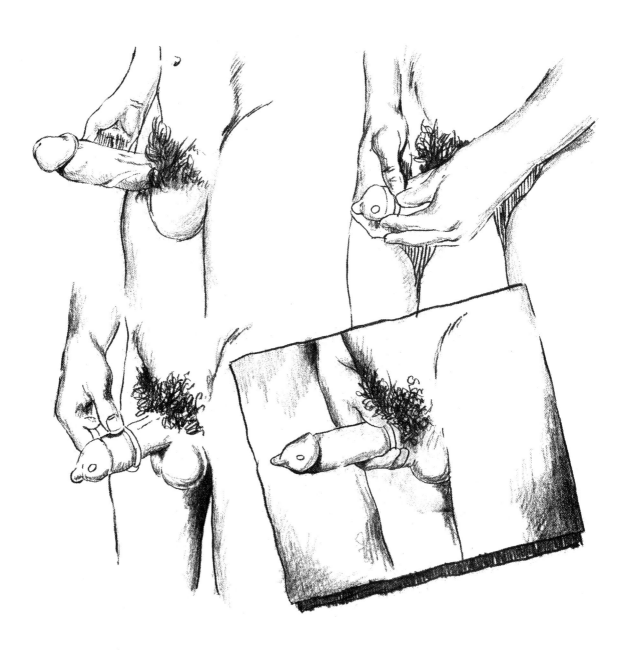

trash. Don't throw it in the toilet; because it won't disintegrate in water, it could clog your plumbing.

If your pubic hairs repeatedly get caught in the condom as you're rolling it off, you can trim or even shave that area.

Varieties of condoms: There are dozens of brands of condoms, some with special features. Experiment until you find what you like best — and then continue to experiment occasionally. The "tickler special" that seems gimmicky now might be just the thing to perk up your sex life next year. The varieties include:

Natural. Some condoms are made from lamb intestines rather than latex. These tend to be more expensive, and they're less elastic than latex brands. They're sometimes reputed to transfer sensations better, but not everyone will notice a difference. Researchers believe that natural condoms do not provide the impervious barrier to HIV that latex does, so they're not a good choice for fucking, though they're still far better than nothing. Because of the preservative used, animal condoms should not be used for oral sex. (One taste, and you won't *want* to use them for that.)

Reservoir tip. Most condom styles provide a narrow protruding tip, which looks like an exaggerated nipple. That's so your semen will have someplace to go. If you use a brand without a reservoir, leave a little space at the end, as you roll it on, for the same purpose.

Adhesive base. If you find the condom tends to pull off or roll up during use, you can get a brand such as Mentor that has a mild adhesive at the base. Just like with a Post-It, the adhesive holds things in place until the job is done, then it readily lets go.

Pre-lubricated. A majority of condoms come with lubrication already on them. This is usually a welcome convenience. Those that are pre-lubricated with a spermicide that contains nonoxynol-9 (and they'll say so, if they are) provide an extra protection against HIV. If you prefer to supply your own lubricant, Gold Circle is a good non-lubricated brand.

Bulb-headed. Also called mushroom-topped, this shape constricts slightly, then widens toward the tip. Some men find it improves the sensation on the head of their penis.

Extra-large. For years, manufacturers advertised that "one size fits all," and it does — latex is remarkably elastic. But for men who are so large that the standard size is uncomfortable, and for men who want others to *think* they're that large, one manufacturer has come out with a larger size. Sure, it may be a marketing gimmick, but isn't it fun to think about those executives sitting in their boardroom, discussing whether to introduce a new condom for men with large cocks? Maxx condoms provide the most room. Other brands that run a bit large include Mentor, Magnum, and Sheik regulars.

Smaller. Although not advertised as such, some condoms have a smaller circumference than others. If your current brand seems a bit loose, experiment until you find a better fit. Manform Plus, Sheik Featherlite, Arouse, Chapeau Blackys, and Zero O brands are among the snugger-fitting brands. Some men report that tighter condoms act something like a cock ring, making their erections harder and giving them more intense orgasms.

Flavored or colored. You can get condoms in any color from pastel blue to hot pink, and an equally wide range of flavors, though you're more likely to find them in a sex shop than at the neighborhood drugstore. If this particular sales gimmick appeals to you, try it. Just be forewarned that the coloring agent may be a cheap dye that doesn't wash out of sheets easily.

Scented. Another sales gimmick, but not quite as harmless. Some people will be allergic to these scents, and the chemicals used could easily irritate your partner's mouth or anus. If you like scents, put on some cologne before you jump into bed.

Textured. Certain brands feature ribs, bumps, and other textures. These are for your partner's benefit, so find out from him whether he likes them.

Spermicides and condoms: Studies have found that some spermicides, used in birth control, also kill the Human Immunodeficiency Virus (HIV) and stop other sexually transmitted diseases. The spermicide ingredient with the best record for killing HIV is nonoxynol-9. This substance has been extensively tested for vaginal use. There's less information about using it anally; however, there is no indication at this writing that it is harmful, and AIDS researchers believe that by using a condom along with a spermicide that includes nonoxynol-9, you'll greatly reduce the risk of transmitting HIV. As with so many aspects of AIDS medicine, medical thinking on this subject could change. If you're sexually active, find a reliable way to stay informed of new knowledge about AIDS prevention. Reading a good local gay newspaper, or a national magazine like *The Advocate,* is the best way to stay abreast of new information.

Some men never get to like wearing a condom. If you're one of them, there are plenty of ways to have fun with a partner that don't require one. But don't assume you fit into this category just because sex with a condom doesn't immediately feel the same as sex without one. Your body has grown accustomed to certain types of sexual stimulation, and anything new will require time to adapt. Don't be too quick to cut yourself off from new experiences.

Condom care: Heat, age, and heavy use can all weaken a condom, increasing the risk of breakage. It's fine to pop one into your wallet or back pocket if you plan to use it that evening, but avoid prolonged storage in a warm spot. That means don't keep one in your wallet or pocket indefinitely, nor next to the radiator, nor in the glove compartment of your car.

If you use your condoms within a year or two after buying them, you shouldn't have to worry about them being too old. If you find one in the bottom of your drawer, and have no idea how long it's been there, it's wise to use it when masturbating, or throw it out.

Of course, never reuse a condom. During a long session, it makes sense to switch to a new rubber midway; there's a lot of abrasiveness in anal sex.

CONSENT. Most sex-positive individuals today believe that any sexual activity between two consenting people is moral and ethical, and should be legal. (The sex-negative individuals don't even think you should be reading this book.)

The disagreements arise over the definition of *consent,* especially as it relates to young people. For centuries, statutory-rape laws have held that below a certain age (sixteen in many states), a child isn't old enough to truly consent to sex. Any adult who has sex with someone under the age of consent is presumed to have committed rape.

Many gay men adhere to this same principle, and look with disdain on men who enjoy sex with adolescents. Others, most vocally the North American Man/Boy Love Association, believe that inter-generational sex is fine, and that all age of consent laws should be abolished.

Advocates on both sides often seem to be setting rules for the entire population simply by extrapolating from their own personal experiences or preferences. Those who, as teenagers, had sex with an older man tend to assume that everyone else's experiences will be as good, or as bad, as their own. The gay men who are most anxious to vilify boy-lovers are often just happy to find someone below them on the pecking order of social prejudice.

At the same time, too many advocates of man/boy love gloss over the very real ethical issues involved. Adults *do* have more power in our society than young people do. These power differences, whether rooted in money, status, physical size, or experience, can quickly cloud the issue of true consent. For these ethical reasons, and because many men are sitting in prison right now for nothing more than providing an orgasm for a willing teenager, you should give the matter careful thought before you have sex with anyone who may be under the age of consent in your state. (See also *Pedophilia*.)

CRUISING. (Looking for a sex partner, in a public area.)

The chief element in cruising is eye contact. As you walk down the street, you don't normally make eye contact with pedestrians walking past you — unless it's a man who appeals to you. If he doesn't quickly reciprocate, then you look away. But when a man does return your look, and your eyes briefly lock, then the chances are he's also interested.

If you're bold, and you're in a gay neighborhood, you might simply stop walking and start a conversation. A more conservative approach is to pause and look in a store window, or walk over to him, if he's stopped walking. One of you can start a conversation with any opening that comes to mind — "This store always has some great clothes on display" — and see where things lead.

Some men will be eager to head for the apartment of whoever lives nearest. Many, however, will suggest getting a drink or cup of coffee first. This gives both of you a chance to learn a bit more about one another. If you don't like what you find out, you're under no obligation to go further. "I hadn't realized it was so late. I have to go finish my laundry," may not be completely honest at this point, but it's a socially acceptable white lie.

Where to cruise: Certain institutions were created to facilitate cruising: many gay bars, and all gay baths, are obvious examples. People will be cruising at any place where gay men congregate: from the annual gay pride march to the gay neighborhood cafe.

In addition, every urban center has an area that's not gay identified, but which is popular for this purpose. Often it's a park, sometimes an all-night diner, library, highway rest area, or bus station. Large beaches often have a gay section, somewhere away from the crowds. In those areas that afford some privacy, sex may happen right there. In others, you go home together.

Timing is critical. Many an urban park that's full of families by day comes alive at night, when it's officially closed, with men looking for sex. The dark provides privacy — you can hear someone approaching before they get close — and makes it hard to be overly discriminating about physical appearances. Some diners become very cruisy on a certain weeknight; perhaps a gay group that meets nearby drops in after their meeting. In a small town, there might be one night on which gay people go to the normally straight bar.

Cruising, however, isn't confined to designated areas. Men cruise each other every day in every imaginable public place: department stores, libraries, supermarkets, parks, and just walking down the street.

Safety: Cruising has its perils, but common sense and a dose of caution will go a long way. The most obvious hazard is the vice squad. Arrests are less common than they were a few decades ago, but they still happen. You may feel you never passed over the line of just being friendly, but if a cop says you propositioned him, it's your word against his in court. Find out from friends who have been around just what the situation is locally.

In addition, there are thugs who prey on gay men. They'll get you into a secluded area, then rob you; or take down your license plate, and later show up to blackmail you.

There's also the danger of expressing your interest too strongly in a man who doesn't reciprocate it. If he doesn't return your eye contact very quickly, drop it. Otherwise Mr. Gorgeous may decide to prove his masculinity by giving you a bloody nose. (See also *Bars; Baths; Beaches; Opening Lines.*)

CRUSHES. Week after week, you can't get him out of your mind. You fall asleep fantasizing about him. You daydream about him at work. Knowing that he's there makes you happier than words can express, yet you're sad that he's not with you every minute. These all-consuming, bittersweet feelings are commonly known as a crush.

Everybody knows that teenagers get crushes. Crushes and short-lived romances are essential steps in learning about love, sex, and the delicious relationship between the two.

Gay people, because we often never got to explore our sexual identity as teenagers, often go through this learning process at an older age. Sometimes at a much older age.

It's common, as you come out, to have a crush on someone who doesn't reciprocate your feelings. Unfortunately, the starry-eyed behavior that can be so endearing in a fifteen-year-old quickly looks silly in a fifty-year-old. If the object of your affection shows no interest in you, don't think that finding you in avid pursuit will change his mind. You'll merely chase him away, and later find yourself embarrassed by your behavior. (See also *First Love.*)

CULTURAL STANDARDS. This is a sex handbook, not a sociology manual. Space doesn't permit a lengthy description of the tremendous range of sexual practices that have been accepted in other times and places. But it's good to keep in mind just what a wide range that has been.

Most of us, even if we're happily gay, at some point feel doubts about our erotic impulses: "Maybe I really am sick for wanting to get spanked ... I know they say it's okay to masturbate, but does anybody else jerk off as much as I do? ... I probably shouldn't spend so much time in my room drawing guys with hard-ons..."

In fact, just about every sexual variation you can imagine has been standard behavior at some time and place. Ancient Greece is famous for its man-boy relationships, and many Pacific cultures have expected boys to have sex with adult men. Piercing and cutting parts of the body has been common in cultures as diverse as ancient Egypt and Native American tribes — Mayan kings pierced their penises with the spine from a stingray. Many works of art that hang in museums today were originally painted or sculpted to satisfy the erotic urges of the creator. (St. Sebastian, naked and pierced by arrows, became a popular image not because he was especially important, but because so many artists wanted to draw him.) Transvestism was common in Greek and Roman cultures, among many others; the emperor Heliogabalus spent his entire four-year reign in drag. Six percent of the ancient Peruvian art that has been unearthed depicts sex between humans and animals.

Just because a certain activity was popular in another society doesn't make it acceptable by the standards that most of us hold today. Some cultures have been into head-hunting, after all. But at times it can be reassuring to know that, whatever your proclivity, you've had plenty of company over the years.

D

DATING. Right through the 1970s, and into the early 1980s, it was customary for two gay men who met and felt an attraction for one another to have sex at the first available opportunity. Sometimes a relationship developed; sometimes it didn't.

Today, many men still do that, and provided you show good sense about safer sex, there's no reason not to. But the trend is toward dating: Spending some time with a man, and getting to know more about him, before deciding whether the relationship should progress to the bedroom. For the newly-out man, this approach is healthy in more ways than one.

Initiating a date: There's a line, though not always a clear one, between asking a man for a date, and inviting him to do something with you as a friend.

If you're going out with someone as a friend, you'll usually each pay your own way. You'll each feel welcome to bring other friends along — in fact, encouraging the other man to "bring a friend, if you like," is a simple way to communicate just how you perceive this relationship.

A date involves just the two of you. Usually the man who does the asking will pick up the tab. If you ask a man for a date, you're implying at least a potential romantic interest. You'll avoid some awkwardness later if you try to get some sense of the guy before you begin dating. Lots of men will be good company for five minutes but after an hour, you'll realize you're totally incompatible.

When you're dating, be sure to note his other interests. Does he like to go to baseball games? Opera? Hiking? Movies? Cooking gourmet dinners at home? Dancing? Any mutual interest of this sort will provide a good opportunity to ask him out again. Don't suggest an activity that you really don't enjoy, just because he does. His company might be so wonderful that you'll have a good time once, but ultimately, this is a dead end.

If you want to get together again, say so after the first date. But as even Amy Vanderbilt could tell you: Don't promise to call unless you mean it.

DENIAL. No one alive today has ever been dead. This cheerful and self-evident observation has a troublesome corollary: None of us can really imagine a world without us. Most of us, unless we're already in a life-threatening situation, don't really believe we could die except of old age. We fantasize about being in a plane crash that has only one survivor and, of course, that survivor is us. We think we can occasionally take a chance with high-risk sexual activities and not get infected with AIDS. By the time we realize otherwise, it's too late.

What's the point of this little lecture? At some point, you're going to meet a man who's dying to fuck your brains out but just doesn't like condoms. He'll convince you that they aren't really necessary. Or he'll become so bristly when you raise the subject that you drop it. Or you'll be so taken by him that you won't even want to bring it up.

A great many men have taken that chance, and would now give anything if they could turn back the clock and start over. Don't become one of them.

DENTAL DAM. (A small square of latex which, like a condom, prevents transmission of viruses and bacteria.)

Nobody except dentists had ever heard of dental dams in pre-AIDS days. But it turns out that they will nicely block the transmission of disease, just as condoms do, in sexual contact that doesn't involve a penis. For gay men, this means rimming.

A dab of lubricant, smeared on the latex where it will come into contact with your anus, will increase sensation significantly. Your partner won't get the same taste as before, of course, and it will feel different to his tongue, but he can still revel in the smell.

Dental dams are recommended in theory more than they get used in practice. Partly, that's because they don't conveniently stay in place by themselves like a condom does. Partly, it's because few of us live near a neighborhood dental-supply store. As demand increases, however, dental dams are increasingly available in sex shops and by mail.

DEODORANTS. Most adult males need some artificial help in order to still smell good at the end of a warm day. Yet if that day ends with sex, there are few greater turn-offs you could provide your partner than letting him lick an armpit and get a dose of some unknown metallic chemical.

The simplest solution, which has other benefits as well, is simply to shower before having sex. Any new sweat that you work up during foreplay should just make him more eager; it's only after perspiration sits on your skin for a time that the foul-smelling bacteria develop. If that's not feasible, then shower just before you head out for the evening, and go light on the deodorant, or find a brand that is as natural as possible.

DILDO. (A device used to simulate — and often to stimulate — the penis.)

Dildos have a long history. Not long after they learned to fashion clubs from large tree branches, our cave-dwelling ancestors undoubtedly made dildos from the smaller branches. In classical Greece, artificial penises fashioned of wood or leather were practically a household commodity. A play from the third century B.C. opens with one woman trying to borrow a dildo from another, only to find that it's already been loaned to someone else.

The popularity continues, although latex and plastic have replaced the wood and leather of yore. Gay men usually insert dildos anally, and move them so as to stimulate the prostate gland, in tandem with masturbation. This provides the pleasure of anal intercourse, without the worries about HIV transmission. It also allows a man who enjoys the feeling of being penetrated to fully control the rate and rhythm of action, as well as the size.

Varieties: The standard dildo looks like an erect penis — usually a very large one — but some consist of just a large smooth cylinder, rounded at the end. It should be pliant, rather than made of hard plastic. There are endless variations, not all of which represent improvements:

Vibrating. Some battery-powered dildos vibrate. These can be used to stimulate the balls and penis, as well as the anus. Provided you don't use them to the point of causing discomfort, they're fine, and for some men, they'll trigger an intense orgasm that can't be achieved any other way. Avoid models that plug into a wall socket; that's just too much voltage for anything that's inside your body. You don't want your safety to be dependent on the quality-control of a dildo factory.

Super-size. Twelve-inch dildos are fine to fantasize about, but not to insert full-length into your ass; there's too much danger of them hitting, and tearing, the rectal wall as it curves around.

Shapable. A dildo that's pliant is better than one that's rigid, but avoid one that will *hold* a new shape when bent or twisted. It's probably got a wire inside, and if that wire breaks through the sheath, it's going to cause serious injury. Ditto for one that can be twisted by means of a handle at the base.

Inflatable. Another bad marketing idea. These devices start out the size of a large penis, then get further inflated once inside you. One could do real damage if it burst.

Double-headed. A double-headed dildo, plus a certain amount of contortion, allows you and a friend to both be fucked at the same time. Read the section below about using a dildo with a partner. The same potential difficulties apply to double-headed dildos. As he thrashes around in the throes of orgasm, you don't want your companion twisting the dildo in such a way that it hurts you. As long as you keep that in mind, there's no reason not to enjoy this variation.

Wide-based. It's best to use a dildo that has a wide handle or base (often in the shape of balls), so that it can't accidentally be inserted all the way in. Lacking that, be careful not to push it too far. "It sounds stupid, but it did happen to me once," says Bill. "Jim and I just got carried away, and I wanted to push it a little deeper, and it was so slippery, I lost my grip. We got it out, but it took twenty minutes and we sort of lost the mood of the evening."

Improvising: There's no need to purchase a dildo. Many other items can serve as well. But use common sense in selecting a substitute. Anything that could break is obviously out of the question. So is anything that could scratch you. Wooden objects (a broom handle, for example) carry a substantial risk of splinters. A less obvious hazard comes from items like Coke bottles. If you insert an empty bottle open-end first, it may slide in fine, but when you try to pull it out, you'll create a suction that holds it in place, and that can damage your insides if you pull too hard.

Carrots, cucumbers, and candles are among the most common items used in place of store-bought dildos. They're all suitable. Vegetables should be washed first, and you may wish to cut them to the desired shape. Some people find their insides get irritated by the skin on a cucumber or zucchini; rolling a condom over the vegetable will take care of that.

Avoid anything with a pointed end. If you're using a tapered candle, round off the base and insert that end, not the top. And now, here's a tip Heloise never gave you: Popping a carrot into a pan of boiling water for a couple of minutes, then allowing it to cool a bit, will give it a bit more pliancy and imparts a pleasant warmth that will delight your innards.

Using a dildo: If this is your first experience with anal insertion, pick a time when you can relax without interruptions. A warm bath helps. For a first experience, use a dildo that's no wider than two of your fingers. You can decide later whether you'd like to try something bigger.

Lubricate your anal opening, pushing a little extra lubricant up inside. The easiest position for this is lying on your back. Continue massaging the area, inserting a lubricated finger (with smooth, well-trimmed nails) inside. Now rub more lubricant along the shaft of the dildo, especially at the tip, and push it gently into the opening as you exhale and push out slightly with the anal muscles.

You'll feel resistance at first, but once the dildo passes your sphincter muscle, it will slide more easily. If you feel it stop, do not push harder. You've probably hit a curve in your rectum. Pull out slightly, and try again at a slightly different angle. You don't want to puncture the rectal wall, but as long as you don't force things, you'll be fine.

With a partner: The best policy is to manipulate your own dildo. You know when it starts to hurt, and you can ease back immediately. You don't have to be alone as you do this, though — a companion can be doing the same with his own dildo, or masturbating you, or just enjoying the show.

If you prefer that your partner wield the dildo, tell him if it seems to be hitting something. You'll feel pain well before he feels anything more than a slight resistance. It's easy enough to get carried away when you've having a good time with a hot guy, and this isn't a good time to be high on drugs or alcohol. You both need to be aware of what's happening.

Cleaning: Clean your toy afterward with soap and hot water, then allow it to air-dry. If you roll a condom onto your dildo before use, your cleaning problems will be simplified, though you'll still need to wash off the base.

It's best to use only your own dildo. It's possible to wash sex toys so thoroughly that they can be safely shared, but it's much easier to each have your own, and that allows you to experience penetration simultaneously.

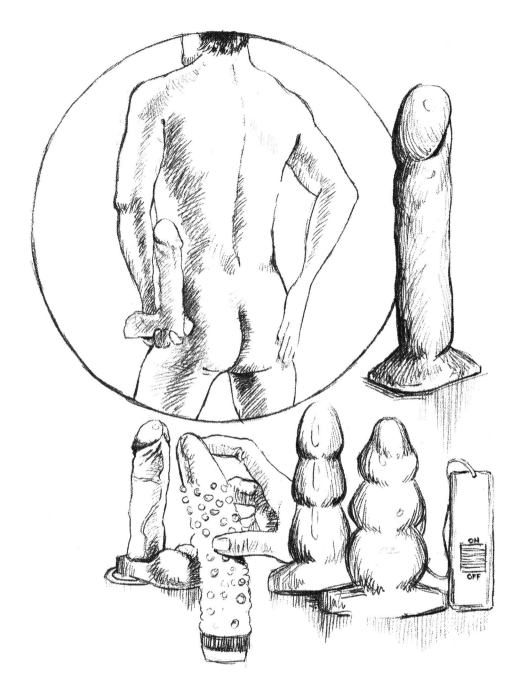

Safety: Should an item get inserted all the way, you can generally work it out on your own. Get in a squatting position, and bear down. Chances are good it will just pop back out. Use plenty of lubricant, and take your time. If the item was a vibrating dildo, however, get to a hospital emergency room right away, even if you're embarrassed. They've seen it before. The batteries in the dildo will probably outlast your rectal wall, and by the time things become painful enough to force you to go for help, it may be too late.

This sounds ominous, but the fact is, millions of people have used dildos in their ass with no problem, and most of them were considerably less informed than you now are. Have fun. (See also *Anal Intercourse.*)

DISABILITIES AND MEDICAL CONDITIONS. For all its electronic scanners, computerized diagnostics, and laser technology, medical science is woefully ignorant about the sexual functioning of people with disabilities, injuries, and diseases. Too many physicians still get sweaty palms when they talk about sex. They take the path of least embarrassment, a path that rarely leads to sexual fulfillment for their patients.

Sexual functioning can be affected by injuries (spinal cord injuries, especially); disease (such as multiple sclerosis, epilepsy, diabetes, some forms of cancer); operations (especially some types of prostate surgery); and prescription drugs (Valium is the #1 culprit, but not the only one).

Psychological factors also play a role. As you recover from an injury or from surgery, if your doctor tells you you'll never enjoy sex again, it's going to be harder for you, even if the doctor has misjudged your physical condition. If an injury or amputation has lowered your self-esteem, you're going to have a harder time, as well.

Rediscovering sex: Many types of accidents can affect your sexual function. But that doesn't mean an end to sex. You may simply need to adjust to new positions or techniques, or learn a new approach to sex — not give it up entirely. In his book *Male Sexuality,* Dr. Bernie Zilbergeld describes a man who was told that he'd never be able to have sex again:

"Paul, a man in his forties with multiple sclerosis, decided to seek therapy after twelve years of no sexual activity. He claimed that his penis was dead but after a while he found that he could get erections with prolonged penile stimulation ... Finally he got around to having sex with a partner. While he continued to need more stimulation than most men, he found some new ways of having his penis stimulated that shortened the amount of time required to get an erection. He also found that he could sometimes have a very good time satisfying his partner and rubbing against her without an erection. Paul is not totally happy. He still wishes he didn't have multiple sclerosis and that he could have sex the way he did before he got the disease. But he's much more content than when we first saw him. When he has sex, he usually enjoys it."

The same operation or disease can affect people differently. Paul become more sexually active than his doctors had seen in other men with multiple sclerosis. Diabetes inhibits erections in some men, but not in others.

Until medical science catches up with reality, don't pay too much attention to statistics about the percentage of men with your condition who reported that they weren't able to have sex. Not too many years ago, psychologists testified that nearly all gay people were mentally disturbed. Social prejudices can put quite a spin on the facts.

Surgery: Physicians learn to cure disease. They aren't always adequately trained to look after other aspects of your well-being. Before undergoing any surgery that could affect your sexual function, ask about such consequences, and what the alternatives are. One form of prostate surgery involves an incision in the perineum (the area between the testes and the anus) that can impede your ability to get an erection. There are other ways to perform prostate surgery that don't involve this side effect, yet — unbelievably — not all surgeons will spell out the options unless you ask.

It's always a mistake to leave your major life decisions to "the experts." Health care is no exception. Ask questions, and read information, until you understand what they're doing and why. Don't hesitate to get a second opinion if you aren't completely comfortable with your doctor, and with the answers you're getting.

Conditions that don't affect sexual functioning: If you're blind or deaf, or have had a colostomy, or you're an amputee, your ability to get an erection and achieve orgasm generally won't be affected, but you'll be different in the eyes of many potential lovers and sex partners.

Some people aren't going to want to form a relationship with you if anything about your physical condition makes them uncomfortable. That's unfair, but it's a fact. In the long term, we can all try to work toward creating a world where that doesn't happen. In the short term, your best bet for happiness is not to worry about such people.

However, don't confuse ignorance with prejudice. Our culture doesn't provide many opportunities for people to learn about what it's like to be physically different from the majority. The burden of this education should not fall on you, but a willingness to shoulder it anyway will open many doors and opportunities.

For many people with a disability, another issue arises when they realize that some individuals are turned on by that specific disability. It's unnerving to learn that a condition that has created obstacles in your life is fetishized by someone else. Yet most relationships start with a superficial physical attraction. Is there really a difference between someone being interested in you because you're an amputee, and being interested because you look like a college jock?

DOUCHING, ANAL. See *Enema.*

DRUG USE. You won't find a long "Just Say No" lecture here. My opinion is that someone who knows what they're doing can occasionally use certain drugs for recreational purposes, and it won't do them any harm. But millions of lives have been ruined — and many have been ended entirely — through drug use. By lumping all drugs together as equally horrible, the New Puritans send out the message that if you've smoked a little dope, then you may as well progress to crack, because drugs are all basically the same. Nothing could be further from the truth.

You've probably already decided whether to experiment with drugs; in any case, a few paragraphs here won't sway your decision. If you are using drugs, be sure you know something about the drugs you're using, and their effects, *before* they go into your body. Even then, you'll be in for some surprises. Many recreational drugs affect people in different ways; and with illegal substances, you can never be sure of just what you're getting. So do your experimentation in a comfortable and safe environment, with people you trust.

Another important precaution about drugs is that, like alcohol, they will affect your judgment and your perceptions of reality. This isn't a good time for sex with strangers. If you want to combine sex and drugs, stick to people who you know will share your concerns about safer sex.

Injected drugs create a new danger: infected needles. Sharing a needle for drug use turns out to be a highly effective way of spreading AIDS. Don't share needles. If you feel you must use a non-sterile needle, clean it between users by rinsing with bleach, then thoroughly rinsing with water.

Amphetamines (Speed): These substances speed up your bodily functions, and thus enhance physical sensations. Someone on speed can get intensely involved in any activity, from having sex to dancing, but it generally impedes erections and orgasms.

Amphetamines are very addictive; withdrawal is a painful and difficult process. They are especially hazardous for people with high blood pressure or cardiovascular problems.

Amyl Nitrite (Poppers): Once widely used by gay men, poppers became less popular as questions arose about their safety, and they are now illegal. They cause a brief rush of blood to the head, which intensifies physical sensations but weakens erections. (See full description under *Poppers*.)

Cocaine: Some men claim that cocaine is great for sex, others disagree. It enhances the sensations of foreplay and fondling, but inhibits erections. During sex, some men prefer to rub it on the penis, nipples, and other erogenous areas, rather than snorting it.

Cocaine is not thought to be physically addicting but the psychological addiction that comes with regular use can be just as devastating.

Marijuana: Many users find that light marijuana smoking heightens their physical sensitivity, and helps them focus on sensations that they'd otherwise not notice. Others say it destroys all interest in sex. Like alcohol, pot lowers inhibitions, and thus can give the impression of being an aphrodisiac. Being heavily stoned, however, will kill interest in sex for just about everybody.

Marijuana is not physically addicting, though it can become psychologically addicting. Some authorities believe that long-term use leads to mental deterioration, but at this point, that is just speculation. Frequent smoking is known to cause lung cancer.

Opiates: Drugs such as morphine and heroin tend to hog the brain's "pleasure receptors"; you're not likely to be interested in sex, food, or any other physical pleasures while using them. You won't even care about taking care of yourself. This results in the burned-out look so characteristic of heroin users.

Psychedelics: LSD and other psychedelics (psilocybin and mescaline) distort the way you perceive reality. Some people enjoy sex in this altered state; most lose interest. The majority of people who take these drugs have pleasurable trips, but some feel panicked and isolated. Bad trips are most common for people who are tense or fearful about the experience, but there's no sure way to tell in advance whether you'll have one.

Because they alter your judgment so dramatically, there's a danger of lapsing into unsafe sex while using psychedelics. Flashbacks and instances of people jumping out of windows while on LSD are much rarer than the media might suggest, but they do occur.

Steroids: Although they aren't recreational drugs, steroids are prevalent in the gay community. They're dangerous. They can cause aggressiveness and other personality changes. They've also been tied to liver cancer and reduced sex drives.

E–F

EARS. Most men get excited by having their ears nibbled, licked, or tongued during lovemaking. Experience will show what your partner likes best. Blowing gently across the ear can also be a turn-on. Never blow forcibly into the ear; doing so can damage the eardrum.

Of course, to make this really enjoyable, you both need to keep those ears thoroughly clean.

EJACULATION. (The sudden discharge of semen from the penis, usually during orgasm, commonly referred to as *shooting, coming,* or *cumming.*)

Ejaculation begins when your prostate gland and other organs respond to increasing sexual tension by contracting, thus forcing sperm and seminal fluid into the urethra. It's this contraction that gives you the feeling "I'm about to come." A few seconds later your pelvic muscles contract, pushing the semen out of your cock.

Why does it so often just ooze out for us mortals, while for porn stars it shoots several feet? Your age, how long it's been since you last had sex, and how long the tension has been building up this time, all play a part. Many men climax more intensely — and most shoot farther — when masturbating themselves, than when a partner does it. That's because they know what their body likes best, and they're getting instant feedback as they proceed.

Porn performers generally abstain from sex for two or three days before a shoot. Some of them believe that certain foods help their performance; milk, celery, and zinc supplements each have their adherents, but there's no scientific evidence that any food affects semen production.

The biggest factor in the porn stars' favor is that it's easier to fake things on film than in real life. (Ever notice what tapioca pudding looks like? Hmmm...) And film producers have one further advantage: they can always wait a couple of days, and do a retake. (See also *Orgasm; Sexual Response Cycle.*)

ENEMA. (A cleansing of the anus and lower rectum by flushing it out with water, also known as an *anal douche.*)

Most gay men have no interest in anal douches. But some prefer to fuck a partner who's just had an anal douche, because it eliminates most contact with fecal matter. Others like to have one before being fucked. It's merely a matter of preference.

Getting an enema: Drug stores sell the basic equipment: a plastic bottle or bag to hold the water; a hose with a valve or clip to control water flow; and a nozzle at the end of the hose, which you'll lubricate, then insert into your ass.

Most kits include instructions. Simply fill the bag with lukewarm water — it should feel neither hot nor cold when it's inside you. Sit on the toilet and hang the bag so it's about level with the top of your toilet tank. Gently insert the nozzle, then let a little water in. Go slowly; when you feel full, take the nozzle out and empty yourself into the toilet. Your intestine is a long and winding organ. You'll probably need to walk around a bit, and have a couple more bowel movements, before all the water is out.

Safety: There's no harm in an occasional enema. A few health practitioners believe they promote good health by clearing accumulated wastes out of your body. But don't get one every day — it will interfere with your body's normal routine for ridding itself of wastes.

Never use high water pressure for an enema — don't hang the water bottle higher than your chest, and never connect yourself directly to a faucet. Your insides weren't designed to withstand that kind of pressure.

There's no need to use soap or chemicals for an enema. If your equipment comes pre-filled with a chemical solution, just empty it out and substitute tap water.

ERECTION. (The penis when it is firm and engorged with blood, especially as a result of sexual excitement.)

The penis is filled with soft, spongy tissue. Sexual excitement increases the flow of blood to the penis, making it larger, longer, and firmer, much as a tubular balloon reacts when filled with water. Although you can often get an erection by thinking about sex, erections cannot be consciously controlled. You can't necessarily get one on demand; furthermore, as any teenage boy can attest, they sometimes happen at the worst times and with no apparent reason.

It's not uncommon to lose an erection while you're having sex; during anal intercourse, the man being fucked often gets soft. If you're really turned on by your partner, and if you don't take the situation too seriously, you'll usually get it back. (See also *Genitals; Penis; Sexual Response Cycle.*)

ETHICS. Just a generation or two ago, the mass media called gay people "perverted" and "immoral"; the New Right still uses those terms. We've thoroughly rejected those labels for ourselves, and we're naturally reluctant to apply them to others, lest we exhibit an equally self-centered view of morality.

The concepts of right and wrong still have relevance, however. We simply need more thought about how we apply them. These decisions are individual, and go well beyond the scope of this book. But it can be helpful to see the distinctions that many gay men have evolved.

Ethical and accepted behavior: Among the gay male community, there's a general acceptance of any sexual activity between consenting and informed adults, provided it isn't likely to cause serious harm to either person.

It's pretty clear whether most situations fall into this category. Bondage, S/M, and humiliation, for example, are seen as valid forms of sexual expression by most gay men, even those who don't choose such activities for themselves. Some situations are borderline: Is it possible for a twelve-year-old boy to give a truly informed and voluntary consent to have sex with an adult? What about having sex in semi-public places: does it force possible observers into the role of non-consenting participants?

Ethical but unwise behavior: Activities that meet the above criteria, but which just aren't in the interests of the person doing them, fall into this category. For example, consider the all-too-common man who has defined his "requirements" for a lover so narrowly that he'll never find such a man, and who meanwhile misses out on what's available. Nobody would deny him that right — but it's not a wise choice.

Unethical behavior. Coerced sex is universally condemned in our culture — and it's usually illegal. Rape is the most obvious example. Many S/M activities involve the illusion of force or coercion, but that illusion is created only through prior agreement, and participants in S/M have the option of withdrawing their consent — and thus ending the activity — at any point.

Anything that involves serious bodily or psychological harm is also considered wrong by most people. Knowingly infecting someone with HIV is out of bounds in anybody's book.

Withholding information that could influence your partner's interest in having sex with you deprives him of the chance to give informed consent. If you're in a supposedly monogamous relationship, but decide to have a fling on the side, your new friend has a right to know your situation — he may want no part of such shenanigans.

Grey areas. This leaves many questions on which there's no clear consensus. Is it okay to have a secret affair with a man who's in a relationship? What if you're unsure of your own HIV status and your partner wants you to fuck him without a condom? If you suspect that a man with AIDS is picking people up and having unsafe sex, should you try to tell them? You can get into some pretty heated arguments over these questions. With time, you'll develop your own code of behavior. Until then, don't rush into things you may regret later.

EXCHANGE OF TELEPHONE NUMBERS. A great many men scrawl their phone number on a scrap of paper in anticipation of getting together again with a new acquaintance. The majority of these numbers are never used. Once you understand and accept that, you'll save yourself a great deal of pain.

Why would anyone ask for your number, then never use it? Maybe he meant to, but fell in love with someone else in the meantime. Maybe he never meant to call, but just took your number because it was the easiest way to get away. Maybe he's afraid of romance or intimacy.

Maybe he's come down with crabs.

Maybe he's just a jerk.

Maybe he lost it. But that's the least likely explanation. If he said he'll call and he didn't, then you're just setting yourself up for rejection if you call him.

EXHIBITIONISM. (Sexual gratification that comes from exposing one's genitals to, or having sex in front of, other people.)

Most often, *exhibitionism* implies the act of shocking an unsuspecting individual, often in public, and without expectation of contact. In this sense it's illegal and anyone turned on by this idea is well advised to channel those impulses in another direction.

Many men enjoy the sense of exhibitionism they get with a consenting partner. Kneeling over a partner and jerking off as he watches involves a strong element of exhibitionism. Some couples carry things further: posing for one another, doing a slow strip, or having sex in front of a mirror. A little extra attention to the setting can make this more enjoyable: soft yellow lighting from a candle or fire or incandescent bulb makes skin tones more appealing than a bright fluorescent light. Rubbing your body with baby oil further enhances your appearance. Skin-tight clothes such as lycra tights or Speedo swim trunks contribute to the atmosphere, especially as they are slowly removed.

A Polaroid or video camera adds a new element to exhibitionism. Be careful with any photographic evidence of acts that might be deemed illegal. Police often seize homemade porn as evidence in criminal prosecutions.

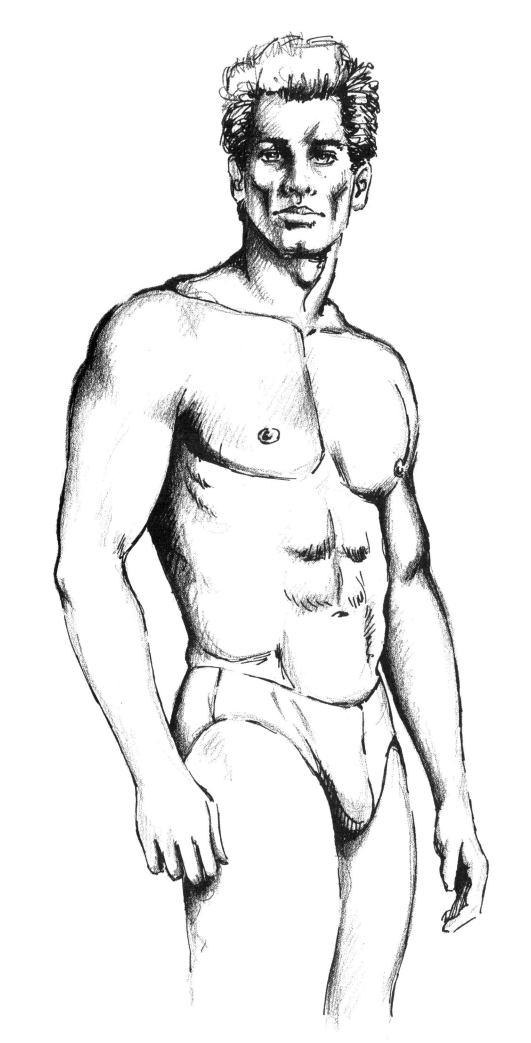

Semi-exhibitionism: A variation of exhibitionism that seems to be common, if not often discussed, involves a small but theoretical possibility of being seen. Men have reported jerking off in front of a window in a dark hotel room, ejaculating onto the street — though this hardly seems fair to pedestrians below, who may have just washed their hair.

Phillip reminisces about his adolescence in the sixties: "On hot summer nights I loved to stand by the side of a little-travelled road after dark, just past a curve, and beat my meat. An oncoming car wouldn't see me until it was practically past me, which meant that if the driver pulled over, I had plenty of time to skedaddle. Actually, only a couple of times did a car even come by, and I was never even sure that I'd been spotted. I suspect that in reality, I moved back into the brush whenever I saw headlights approaching, though I remember myself as being pretty brazen about it all."

This theme of sex that's not actually private, but where no one seems likely to see it, appeals to draw many men. Other experiences that have been reported include:

"At least once a summer my lover and I beat off at the beach, in chest-deep water, about a hundred yards from anybody. We take turns putting on a snorkeling mask so we can watch each other come underwater."

"Occasionally I'll go to a movie on a weeknight, when I know the theater won't be crowded, and sit a little ways off from anybody else and masturbate."

"On trips, my boyfriend and I took turns jacking off when we weren't driving. We never involved the driver — that seems pretty dangerous — and always stayed below the speed limit while anything was going on."

"Some of the hottest sex I ever had was with a guy I met at summer camp after my sophomore year of college. We started fondling each other while everybody was singing by the campfire. We knew there'd be no privacy later in the cabin, so we walked over to the woods, and made love from a spot where we could watch the group."

In a less sex-negative culture, exhibitionism might be legal. While it would seem to involve a non-consenting partner — the surprised observer — that objection reflects a strong anti-sex bias. After all, anyone who sets foot outside is exposed to sights like cigarette billboards that some of us find far more objectionable.

For now, however, public exhibitionism just invites arrest, or even fag-bashing. If you feel the urge to display yourself, it's wisest to involve only people who want to see what you've got to show. That still allows plenty of latitude for mutual enjoyment. (See also *Voyeurism; Mutual Masturbation; Three-Ways.*)

FANTASY. Not so long ago, masturbation was honestly thought to cause all sorts of mental and physical disorders, and the so-called authorities proclaimed that nice people didn't have outrageous sexual fantasies.

That's changing. Most adults fantasize about sexual activities that they'd never want made public. A 1991 study at the State University of New York found that fantasies about such activities as cross-dressing and bondage were "surprisingly common."

It's pretty hard these days to come up with a sex fantasy that would shock or surprise a seasoned sex researcher. Moreover, these researchers believe the fantasies you develop while masturbating can help you develop a more fulfilling sex life, whether alone or with a partner.

Because this subject still is shrouded in secrecy, we don't know just how common various fantasies are. Three themes seem virtually universal: sex with someone other than your lover; sex with a specific celebrity or movie star; and sex in an exotic locale. Other motifs also recur regularly. A few of these, with examples from various men, are listed here. Note how most of these favorite fantasies incorporate several popular themes.

Phallic worship: "I'm the ruler of a large empire. My subjects worship me, and once a year, I allow a special treat for the best-looking men of the kingdom. They gather in the courtyard below my balcony, stark naked, and just before sunset, I walk out above them. I'm naked too. I slowly start to masturbate, and they watch as my cock stiffens. As my hand slides up and down my hard flesh, faster and faster, they get wilder and wilder. They're all excited, too, but none of them is paying attention to their own hard-ons, they're too busy watching me. Finally I feel my cock stiffen, as tight as it gets, and my come shoots out. They crowd under me, their mouths open, clawing to be the one who catches my seed in their mouth. The man who succeeds will be invited into my private chamber later that week."

Power: "I'm a soldier in ancient Sparta. While I'm out on patrol, an enemy soldier sneaks up and tries to kill me. I deflect his spear, and throw him to the earth. We're both naked, of course, as soldiers were back then. Normally, I'd never force anyone to have sex, but as I pin him to the ground, my knees on his shoulders, I decide it's time he learned who's in control. I get hard, and I put my knife to his throat and force him to suck me. Then once I'm really horny, I throw the knife aside — I know I can handle him — and I roughly roll him over. He fights back, but I pin him down and fuck him hard."

Powerlessness: "I've been captured by the Nazis during World War II, and they've turned me over to their eugenicists, because they've decided I have the perfect genes for breeding. They want me to jerk off into a test tube, so they can impregnate a woman with my sperm, but I refuse. They chain me with my back to a huge pillar, and every day one of them comes in and tries to masturbate me, but even though I get erect, I refuse to come. Finally they send in the young captain of the guard, a muscular man with a blond crew cut. He strips off his clothes and starts pumping his dick with one hand, while he sucks me off. I struggle to hold back, and for a long time, I succeed. Then he gasps and starts to shoot on my leg, and I lose it, and pump my load into his mouth. He runs off, presumably to spit it all into a test tube, and I'm left to realize that I've just been used. I'm nothing but a sperm machine for them. Oh, I love it!"

Exhibitionism: "I'm back in college, and there's a compulsory sex education class. The instructor says he needs a volunteer to help demonstrate certain things, and class participation counts for a lot in this course, so I volunteer. He tells me to get undressed. Well, I hadn't anticipated that, but I shyly strip to my shorts. I'm already semi-erect. 'Please keep going, Mr. Thomas,' he says, 'we don't have all day.' So I peel off my shorts and everybody gasps as my cock snaps free. By now I'm completely hard. 'Notice how the head has turned darker, with all the blood being forced into it,' he's saying. 'Now, Mr. Thomas, could you please masturbate for us?' I spit into my palm and thrust my hips forward and get started. The class is all staring straight at my prick, and the instructor keeps pointing things out. Finally I tell him I've just gotta come, and he says okay, and I ejaculate halfway across the room."

The center of attention: "While exploring a remote mountain region, I stumble across an ancient civilization. They've never seen a black man before, and they think I must be a god. I am enthroned in the local palace, and every day, dozens of men come by, hoping to have sex with me. If I'm in a generous mood, I allow each of them to suck my cock for a few minutes, holding off my orgasm until at least half a dozen of them have had the pleasure of servicing me. They all hang around, though, so they can watch as I come."

Taboo topics: Most gay men feel perfectly comfortable with their fantasies except for two subjects: rape, and sex with prepubescent children. One man, who asked not to even be identified by a pseudonym, confided that "ever since my late teens, I've had fantasies about violently ripping my brother's clothes off his body and raping him. The elements of violence and incest in that fantasy bother me, and I don't know why it's so strong for me. It's not something I'd normally tell

anyone about." He expressed concern that by entertaining this fantasy, he'd become likely to carry out something of the sort in real life. Yet, on reflection, he noted that he'd never felt the slightest inclination to actually act in this way.

The connection between fantasy and real-life actions is poorly understood. Some anti-porn crusaders argue that violent fantasies lead to violent acts. This seems to be a case of letting politics dictate one's conclusions. There's no evidence of such a connection, and many therapists believe that, on the contrary, fantasies provide a safe outlet for socially taboo thoughts, actually reducing the likelihood that they'll be acted upon. The best advice at this point is to freely enjoy whatever fantasies turn you on. And regardless of your fantasies, if you feel at times like you can't control your actions and that you may commit rape or child abuse, it's time to get professional help.

FETISH. (An object, substance, or part of the body that produces a sexual response.)

The most common fetishes among gay men involve clothing: jockstraps, white jockey shorts, Speedo swimsuits, football helmets or shoulder pads, boots, or Levis. Fetishes may also center on a part of the body: the feet, nose, ears, or nipples. Others involve a material that can be incorporated into sex play: leather, rubber, latex, or nylon. Or an embellishment: tattoos, a shaved pubic area, or pierced nipples.

Yet other fetishes include: uniforms; dirty underwear; business suits; preppie clothing; bikini underwear; flannel shirts; silk robes; chocolate; bandannas; masks; garter belts; eyeglasses; wingtip shoes; and motorcycles.

How are fetishes formed? If your earliest erotic experiences involve a certain item, it may become a fetish for you. But this doesn't explain most of them, and no one has come up with a satisfactory all-encompassing theory on the subject. Does it really matter?

Enjoying your fetish: Society sends out the message that fetishes are unusual or wrong. Nonsense! Most men have a few fetishes, but the most prevalent ones — being attracted to big pecs, for example — are called turn-ons or preferences. Just think of your fetishes as additional opportunities for sexual enjoyment.

Unless two men meet because of a shared fetish, most fetishes will intrigue one partner while the other feels neutral about it. If you indulge him occasionally, and he indulges you, you'll both be happier for it. But you don't need a partner to enjoy a fetish; most are easily adapted to solo play.

Even in an ongoing relationship, it can be difficult to tell a lover about your fetish. There's always the danger, however small, that he'll be turned off, or will laugh, or will simply be offended that you could fetishize an object when, after all, you have *him*. One way to raise the subject is to ask your partner to name an item of clothing he'd like you to wear the next time you make love. If he says there isn't anything, however, don't assume he's just being reticent. Quite possibly he just prefers you naked.

FINDING A LOVER. The traditional advice about this is still the best: You don't find a lover by looking for one. If you go out in the evening with the goal of finding a lover, your eagerness will turn off anyone worth having. You may occasionally hook up with another man who's equally eager; after a few months, you'll realize that you had nothing else in common.

A better approach is to get involved in activities that you enjoy.

Meet people who share your interests — regardless of whether they seem like potential lovers. Make friends with those you like, whether they're male or female, gay or straight. They'll probably know other single gay men.

This approach comes with no guarantees. But if you don't find a lover by doing the things you enjoy, you probably wouldn't have found one by prowling the bars, either. This way, at least you'll have fun. You may even get some new perspectives on life. In the end, what you get out of life has far more to do with what you put into it than with whether you have a lover at your side. (See also *Alternatives to the Bars.*)

FIRST LOVE. Movies, television, and novels all present "first love" as a magical period of true bliss. Often it is, though the bliss usually lasts longer in the movies than in real life. There is something truly magical about discovering, for the first time, just what happens when sexual attraction and spiritual sharing join forces.

The experience is usually best if you and your lover are both in love for the first time. You won't need to excuse each other's over-enthusiasm in these cases — you won't even notice it.

But, of course, we don't get to choose just how these things work. More often, the object of your first love will reciprocate your general feelings, but it won't be his first time. In that case, you'll each experience the affair differently. He may seem to be holding back, waiting to see how things develop, while you're eager to split the down payment on a new house. He may be less ready to drop what he's doing and change plans on short notice, just so the two of you can be together. That doesn't mean he loves you less. In fact, because he has other experiences to compare this to, he may understand his feelings better than you understand yours.

If you're the more experienced man, and it's your lover who's having his first love affair, you have certain responsibilities. This is a special time of life for him. The relationship may last a lifetime. But more likely, it won't. In that case, what happens between you and him will greatly affect the quality of his future relationships. You'll need to carefully juggle your roles as a more knowledgeable instructor in a learning relationship, and that of the equal partner in a love relationship. That may seem hard. Fortunately, as they say, love makes all things possible.

Realities: As in so many areas of life, money quickly rears its green head when two people fall in love and move in together. It's natural to want to immediately share everything with the object of your love, including income and property. But it's a lousy idea.

My rule of thumb is to wait at least three years in any relationship, and especially in your first relationship, before you consider any income-pooling. Sounds like forever, doesn't it? But if the relationship does in fact last a lifetime, a few years' delay won't make much difference. And if it ends after six months, you'll save yourself a lot of grief and expense.

Before you get too far into the relationship, you also need to discuss your views about monogamy. Many people assume that their ideas on the subject — whether they're strongly in favor, or think it's a silly idea — are the norm, and that their lover must agree with them unless he's indicated otherwise. That's a recipe for disaster.

FISTING. (Inserting the entire hand into a partner's rectum. Also commonly called *fist-fucking* or *handballing*.)

Those hearing about it for the first time express awe that fisting is even possible. But the anus is more elastic than most people have ever had occasion to experience. Although few gay men have tried fisting, regular practitioners claim that it provides a feeling of fullness and satisfaction they can't achieve any other way. It's even been described as "wonderfully relaxing."

Fisting falls into the category of Advanced Sexual Expression. If you're new to gay sex, try other activities first. Walk before you run.

Doing it: Fisting can damage the rectal wall, but the risk of such damage can be kept small.

First, be comfortable with your body, including your anus. Don't try fisting unless you can comfortably accommodate large dildos or cocks into your ass.

Second, learn from an experienced partner — someone you trust, who has good sense, and who cares about your welfare. He should have his nails trimmed close, and very smooth, and should be wearing no rings or jewelry on his hand. He'll start by just inserting one finger, then several, into your anus. Eventually he'll extend his entire hand, squeezing the thumb against the palm, and work it in, making a fist only after his hand is past the sphincter muscle at the anal opening.

Some authorities recommend a thorough enema beforehand, to rid the area of all fecal matter, but others believe that repeated enemas can have harmful effects. It's not a subject that has received a lot of medical research, and you'll have to make your own judgment calls on this one.

Safety: The big danger lies in the possibility that your rectal wall will be torn. One researcher estimates that such perforations happen in roughly one of every 2,000 fistings. In the event of a tear, you *must* get prompt medical attention. Without it, fecal matter will leak into the rest of your body, resulting in peritonitis and a painful death.

How do you know if your rectal wall has been torn? If you're sober, you may sense it, though it won't actually hurt; there are no pain receptors in that part of your body. If you're drunk or stoned, you'll probably have no idea what's happened. But later, up to a day or two after the injury, you're likely to feel severe cramps or fever, possibly accompanied by tiredness and mental confusion. Other symptoms can include glassy eyes, abdominal pain or swelling, and significant bleeding. Light bleeding — just enough to make the lubricant pink — usually indicates just some abraded tissue, and is probably not serious.

Being fisted requires a high degree of relaxation. Unfortunately, many participants achieve that relaxation by heavy drinking or drug use. Don't. On this occasion you must be aware of what's going on during sex, and responsive to your body's signals. Doctors who have treated fisting-induced injuries report that in nearly every case, the patient was heavily drugged or drunk. If you can't enjoy being fisted without chemical aid, find another way to have fun.

Many tops these days wear a latex glove while fisting, to reduce the chances of infection passing in either direction; the glove also protects against scrapes caused by the fingernails. A top wearing a glove should insert his hand only as far as the border of the glove.

Fisting and AIDS: AIDS literature often lists fisting as a high-risk activity for HIV infection. That's misleading. It would be hard to transmit HIV from one partner to another by fisting.

However, the rectal tissue *can* be weakened by the abrasive action of fisting, even if it isn't actually torn. That makes it easier for HIV to enter the bloodstream. Anyone who gets fisted should be especially careful about safer sex. It's advisable not to let anyone fuck you for a few days; if the condom breaks, you'll be more susceptible to infection.

FOOD FANTASIES. Imagine licking whipped cream off your lover's cock, or licking honey from his buns, or smearing chocolate all over your bodies....

Sound like fun? Some highly erotic photographs have exploited just such fantasies.

But in reality, while sex and food both rate high on the pleasure scale, they don't mix well for most of us. Paul and Ralph tried eating strawberries and whipped cream off one another's chest once. "The strawberries were good, but whipped cream is not at its best when licked out of someone's chest hair," recalls Paul. "Overall it was a reasonably pleasant little dessert, and we laughed a lot as we did it, but we'd both lost our hard-ons by the time we finished. We showered and went to bed without ever getting around to sex."

However, a few men do find the combination to be a real delight. You won't know if you're one of them until you try it, will you?

FORESKIN. (The extra skin at the tip of the penis on an uncircumcised man.)

On an uncircumcised man, the foreskin covers the head of the penis when it's soft. The foreskin retracts during sex, when the penis is hard, thus exposing the head. Some men assert that uncircumcised cocks are more sensitive, because the head is protected most of the time. This is strictly a matter of conjecture; hardly anyone gets to experience it both ways. (See also *Circumcision.*)

FRENCH KISSING. See *Kissing.*

FROTTAGE. (Rubbing the penis between one's own body and a partner's body, often colorfully called the *Princeton Rub.*)

This position seems to have derived its nickname, and perhaps its popularity, from college lads who enjoyed sex together but felt that by avoiding penetration or manual touch, they weren't really being homosexual. Gee, boys, could you explain that again?

Meanwhile, here's what they're doing. One lies on top the other, face-to-face, usually with lubricant spread in the critical areas. (A side-by-side position is possible, but it's harder to maintain adequate pressure.) Then they just start rubbing up and down, pushing and thrusting with the pelvis, in whatever combination feels best. The resulting sensation brings some men quickly to orgasm, and does nothing at all for others.

Safety: Frottage is about as safe a time as two men can have in bed. As with masturbation, there's a small theoretical possibility of transmitting HIV if one man ejaculates on an open cut or sore of the other. There's no evidence that anyone ever got AIDS this way, and no reason whatsoever to worry about it.

FUCKING. See *Anal Intercourse; Intercourse.*

G–H–I

GAY BARS; GAY BATHS. See *Bars; Baths.*

GENITALS. (Sex organs.)

The most obvious and most talked-about of the male sex organs is, of course, the *penis.* Three layers of soft spongy tissue run the length of the penis, just under the skin. (You can see one of these tube-shaped layers running along the bottom of your penis when you have an erection.) Sexual excitement causes this tissue to fill with blood. It pushes against the harder surrounding tissue and causes an erection, just as pumping air into a bicycle tube causes the surrounding tire to become firm. The penis has no bones or muscles in it, though there are muscles at the base, inside your body, which contract during an orgasm. Nor, as you've probably noticed, does it have a brain.

The penis extends well into the body, to a bulb-shaped ending that lies close to the anus. The stroking motion transmitted to this bulb is, for some men, a source of pleasure when being fucked.

In most men the head of the penis is more sensitive than the shaft, and the ridge at the base of the head is most sensitive of all. On uncircumcised men, the foreskin is also highly sensitive.

The *testes* are the other external organ. These two glands, each about the size of a walnut, lie in the *scrotum,* a loose sac of skin that acts as a temperature regulator. In colder weather (or in a swimming pool, where heat is constantly drawn from the body), the scrotum contracts and pulls the testes up against the body, to take full advantage of body warmth. As the temperature rises, the scrotum relaxes, lowering the testes away from your body heat. The point of all this is to keep your sperm, which are produced in the testes, from being damaged by extremes of temperature.

Undescended testes are not uncommon, but should get a doctor's attention — they can be a cancer risk. Should you need to get one removed for any reason, it's a fairly simple procedure to have a prosthetic testicle implanted in the scrotum.

Several more organs lie inside the body. The *prostate gland,* which lies just in front of the rectum, secretes most of the fluid that makes up your semen. The prostate is often stroked (through the rectal wall) during anal intercourse; this creates an especially pleasurable feeling for some men, and can move them more quickly toward orgasm.

Other glands — the small Cowper's gland, and the seminal

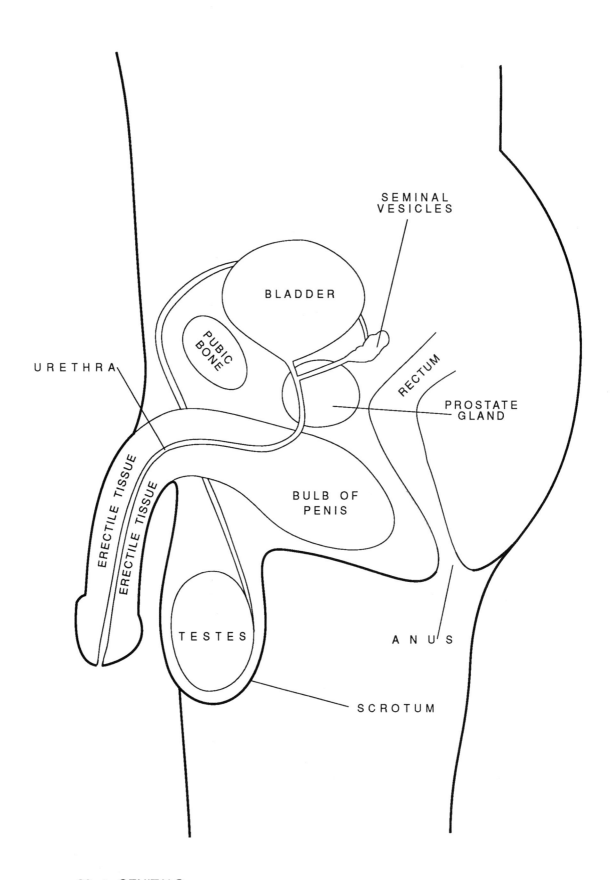

SEMINAL
VESICLES

BLADDER

PUBIC
BONE

URETHRA

RECTUM

PROSTATE
GLAND

ERECTILE TISSUE

ERECTILE TISSUE

BULB OF
PENIS

TESTES

ANUS

SCROTUM

vesicles — also secrete small amounts of fluid, but knowing more about them won't do one thing to improve your sex life. (See also *Penis; Sexual Response Cycle.*)

GOLDEN RULE. "Do unto others as you would have others do unto you."

The Golden Rule is a good starting point for sex, as for other aspects of life. But in the case of sex, it requires an extra step.

Most men instinctively perform on their lover what they enjoy having done to them. If you like having your ears nibbled, you'll nibble his. If you like squeezing the base of your cock as you jerk off, you'll squeeze his. That would be fine if we were all made the same way. Since we're not, you need to go an extra step. You want him to do, to you, the things you like best. Do likewise.

A good starting point is to watch each other masturbate. Notice what he likes to do. Also pay attention to what he does to you as he jerks you off. Unless he's read this book first, that's probably what he'd like.

Another way to communicate all this is that old standby: talk to each other. Gay men tend to be pretty up-front about just what we do and don't like in bed.

HANDKERCHIEF CODE. (A way of defining one's sexual interests by means of a colored handkerchief.)

The use of colored bandannas or handkerchiefs as a sexual code originated many years ago. They were more useful, and more popular, at a time when it was riskier to start a conversation about such things. However, the code still has its advocates. Generally, wearing the handkerchief in the left rear pocket means the wearer wants the role usually considered "dominant" or "active"; in the right rear pocket, it means he wants that done to him. In the listing below, the first definition is for the left pocket; the second is for the right. The first five are the most common.

Navy blue. Wants to fuck (have anal intercourse); wants to be fucked.

Red. Wants to fist-fuck; wants to be fist-fucked.

Black. Top, heavy S/M; bottom, heavy S/M.

Grey. Top, light S/M or bondage; bottom, light S/M or bondage.

Yellow. Watersports active — wants to piss on someone; wants to take someone's piss.

Light blue. Wants to be sucked; wants to suck cock.

Orange. Top, will do anything; bottom, will accommodate anything. (These days, anybody who flies an orange flag is likely to be thought crazy or stupid.)

Green. Hustler.

Many more codes have evolved; some reference lists define dozens. Only those above are widely used.

Do not assume that you're always interpreting a colored handkerchief as the wearer intends. Some men simply like the look — or they just have a runny nose. Teenage boys in some cities have taken to sticking a red handkerchief in their pocket because they've seen it done and think it looks cool — they'd be horrified if they knew how it was being interpreted. For better or worse, a piece of cloth does not eliminate the need for one-to-one communication.

HIV. (The Human Immunodeficiency Virus, generally believed to cause AIDS.) See *AIDS*.

HIV STATUS. If you're infected with HIV — the virus believed to cause AIDS — your body will eventually respond by creating antibodies to fight the virus. Medical laboratories can test your blood to see if these antibodies are present. If they are, then you're assumed to be infected with HIV, and you're considered to be *HIV-positive*. (HIV itself is more difficult to detect.) If antibodies are not present, you're considered *HIV-negative*.

Because modern treatments help people even in the earliest stages of HIV infection, this test is recommended for anyone who believes they could have been exposed to AIDS. It's not foolproof, however. In a very small number of cases, often as a result of human error, the results are simply wrong.

Other times, the results are misleading: If you were infected with HIV recently, antibodies probably haven't had time to form. Getting a second test six to twelve months after the first one — provided that you haven't been exposed to AIDS in the meantime — is the best way to confirm the results.

Unfortunately, this HIV-antibody test has led to a new form of discrimination in the gay community. Many personal ads in gay newspapers now indicate, "GM, HIV-positive, seeks same" or "GM, HIV-negative, seeks others of same status...." These men seem to have decided that we should all sleep only with people who share our HIV status. It's sad to see yet another division created in our community.

It's also dangerous.

Both groups believe that by having sex only with partners of the same status, they can eliminate the need for safer sex. The negative-seeks-negative adherents assume that you can know your own HIV status, and that of your partner, with reasonable certainty. As discussed under *Risk Management*, it's tricky enough to be sure of your own status, much less that of your partner.

For couples who both test positive, there's also some uncertainty. Most authorities urge such couples to still follow safer-sex guidelines, because re-infection (especially if it's by someone with a different strain of the virus) can probably hasten the onset of full-blown AIDS. (See also *AIDS*.)

HOME MOVIES. The electronic revolution has opened up several new approaches to sex. Home sex videos are among the most popular.

The technology of home videos is best learned from your owner's manual. Once you understand the mechanics, you've got several approaches open to you.

Phillip and Jason keep it simple. Phillip already had a video camera, and has used it several times to record Jason sprawled in bed, beating off. Later they watch these clips together, and occasionally they've invited a third man over for home movies and sex.

They've also set the camera on a stand, focused right where the action will be, and gone to it, doing their best not to look at the camera. "It's fun to watch these later, but with the stationary viewpoint, they do look *very* much like the home movies they are," notes Phillip. "We miss some good shots — if you'll pardon the pun."

For a more polished result, get a friend or two involved. This can be as simple as having someone record a lovemaking session between you and your partner, or you can write out a script and try to produce a video that will compete with those you've been renting. You should have no trouble finding co-stars; lots of men have always fantasized about acting in a porn film. Happy casting!

For both legal and ethical reasons, do not show such films beyond their originally intended audience without the clear, written permission of all involved. Be discreet — in Great Britain, fifteen gay men were sent to jail in 1991 after Scotland Yard confiscated home videos of consensual S/M activity. Above all, never photograph sexual activity involving anyone under eighteen. It's all too easy to end up in jail. (See also *Pornography*.)

HOTLINE. No, this isn't the number to call when you're hot and horny. (For that, see *Telephone Sex*.) It's the number you can call in many cities for all sorts of information related to being gay.

Gay hotlines, which are often staffed by volunteers, are ready to answer a surprisingly varied range of questions. Most hotlines, for example, could tell you:
  • The address of the nearest gay bookstore;
  • The legal age of consent in your state;
  • How to contact the gay softball league;
  • Where to get a copy of the local gay newspaper;
  • Names and addresses of a few nearby gay bars;
  • The date of the next gay men's chorus concert;
  • Where to go for the HIV-antibody test.

Getting the number: Look in your local phone book under Gay Hotline or Gay and Lesbian Hotline. If there's not one locally, try the nearest larger city. The annually updated *Gayellow Pages* lists nearly every hotline in the country; the *Alyson Almanac* provides numbers for the major cities. (See Bibliography.)

HUMILIATION. (Sexual excitement generated by playing upon erotically charged feelings of being naughty, embarrassed, exposed, or ashamed.)

In its most common form, sexual humiliation consists of calling your partner a cocksucker or bunghole, and talking dirty about how much he enjoys servicing your cock.

Humiliation sometimes appears as a component of S/M sex. The dominant partner hurls epithets and insults at the bottom, or forces the bottom to lick his boots or feet. As with all S/M sex, humiliation in this context is part of the role-playing, and is pleasurable for both parties.

Superficially, it might seem that anyone who enjoys humiliation must suffer from low self-esteem. But emotions don't work so simply. In the hands of most devotees, humiliation is merely one more technique that can be used to augment a sexual encounter. People who like verbal abuse are often proud, together individuals who just want a little vacation from acting so responsible.

HUSTLER. (A male prostitute.)

Many gay men pay for sex. Some simply can't attract the partners they want. Others are drawn by the fact that sex-for-money never involves unexpected emotional attachments; or have specific sexual tastes that are most easily filled by a hustler. A few men get a special thrill from paying for sex.

The world of hustling includes all sorts of men. A few are just glad to get paid for something they enjoy. More often, it's simply a job, albeit one that's illegal and involves certain unconventional risks. Some hustlers are straight, and others will claim they are, but openly gay hustlers are increasingly common. Many hustlers are on drugs.

Hustlers usually hang out in certain areas, often around the bus station or near the gay bars. Once you've expressed interest — which can be accomplished merely by loitering in the same area, gazing into a shop window — a hustler will take it from there. Be sure, before heading off together, that he's willing to do what you want, and that you've settled on his price. Both issues are usually open to negotiation.

Hustlers understandably expect to get paid before having sex, but don't pay until you're in the room together, ready to get undressed. If you pay earlier, he may disappear.

Price: Even more than most businesses, hustling is subject to the vagaries of supply and demand. It's also subject to negotiation. Expect to pay $25 to $50 on the street, double or even triple that if you're answering an advertisement. You'll be in a better position to negotiate if you're not dressed in a fancy suit or driving an expensive sports car.

Safety: Hustlers live in a street-smart world, and many have adopted a "Look out for Number One" attitude. A few suggestions for avoiding trouble:

- If you're a regular customer at a hustler's bar, check him out with a bartender or another customer.
- Trust your instincts if they tell you not to go into a room alone with this guy.
- Don't flash around a lot of cash.
- If you're uncomfortable with him, ask to see his ID. You can explain that you want to be sure he's of age, and that's a good precaution — but in addition, once you know his name, he's less likely to try to pull a fast one.
- Don't try to talk the price down too much, and never try to avoid paying him.
- Don't talk a hustler into performing an act that he seems reluctant about. If it hurts his pride, he may seek revenge later.
- Don't fall asleep after having sex; your wallet and even your clothes could be gone when you wake up.
- Be aware that a few enterprising men take the license numbers of their johns, for future blackmail purposes.

As for really serious crimes: some hustlers have committed assault and murder, but so have boyfriends, lovers, and spouses. The danger of encountering physical violence from a hustler is probably no greater than the risk involved in any sexual encounter with someone you don't know.

There's also a danger from the other end of the legal spectrum. As a form of prostitution, hustling is illegal, though the law is enforced haphazardly. Use discretion.

Health: Protect your health, and his. Assume that a hustler is HIV-positive, regardless of anything he may tell you or any "test results" he may show you. He may also have less serious but nonetheless unpleasant forms of venereal disease. Stick to safer sex.

At the same time, a young hustler may be so eager to please a customer that he won't look after his own health adequately. You won't often find morality preached in this book. But anyone who takes advantage of a hustler's poverty by paying him extra to endanger his health deserves the hottest hell that the right wing has to offer.

High-class hustling: Escort services, masseurs, and models often advertise in gay and alternative newspapers. A few of the masseurs are just what they claim to be; they'll usually stipulate "non-sexual" in their ad. The others are offering sex. (*In* means at their place; *out,* at yours.) They'll charge more than a street hustler, they're less likely to be on drugs, less likely to rip you off, and will usually be in better physical shape — many men work their way through college as a "model."

IMPOTENCE. (The inability to have, or to maintain, an erection.)

Most men suffer from an occasional bout of impotence. It may happen when you're just not that comfortable with a situation or not especially turned on by your partner. Alternatively, it can happen when the man you've been dreaming of for the past two years ends up in your bed, and suddenly nothing seems more important than getting good and hard.

Occasional impotence: A single bout of impotence may be caused by stress of this sort. It could also be that you're coming down with the flu, or had too much to drink.

If it only happens occasionally, accept it as a fact of life. The human body isn't a machine. Your body and mind are influenced by many factors, and most of them are beyond your control.

If you're in bed with a man who's having a bout of impotence, treat him as you'd like to be treated if it were you. Next time, perhaps it will be. A charitable attitude is a wise thing to spread around.

Physical impotence: In a minority of cases, long-term impotence is caused by physical factors. If this is your situation, you'll never get an erection — not while you're masturbating, or dreaming, or upon waking.

Some medications cause impotence. If that's a possible side-effect of a drug you're on, your doctor should have warned you, but doctors make mistakes, so ask. Obesity, diabetes, and excessive alcohol consumption can also contribute. Again, your doctor is the best source of advice. As you get older, erections won't appear as readily, and won't have that man-of-steel quality you remember from your teens, but age in itself does not cause impotence.

Penile implants are available for men suffering from physical impotence. The simplest implant, which has been in use for years, makes your penis permanently semi-hard. It will be rigid enough to enjoy sex (including orgasm and ejaculation) but not so hard that you'll stand out, so to speak, when you change clothes at the gym. A newer implant is more complex: Surgeons insert an inflatable cylinder in your penis, and a bulb in the scrotum that's used to pump up or deflate the cylinder. A knowledgeable doctor can discuss these options in more detail, and can advise you on whether they're appropriate for your situation.

And now, a word about doctors: Even in this day and age, they're not always well informed about sex, and they're not always comfortable talking about it. Especially for older patients, some doctors feel sex isn't that important, so they don't bother to provide the information you need. If some gentle nudging on your part doesn't change this, look around for another doctor. The recommendations of friends are your best source; a local gay paper or hotline may also help. Meanwhile, your pharmacist may be able to provide information about specific drugs, and their effects, if your doctor doesn't.

Psychologically caused impotence: If you sometimes have an erection, but not when you most want to, your problem is a mental one. As you know by now, worrying about it doesn't do any good. The trick is *not* to worry about it, and with a caring partner, that attitude may be less impossible than it sounds.

First, go without sex for at least a couple of weeks. That means no masturbating, either. Now your partner should give you a thorough, gentle massage. You may get an erection. If so, he should ignore it and let it go back down. After he's massaged your body, your partner should progress to your penis and testicles, gently massaging them. If you get hard, he should stop until you're soft again, then resume where he left off. After you've gotten, and lost, several erections, you'll gain confidence that it's not such a big deal after all. Only now, in whatever way you prefer, should he or you bring you to climax.

If this goes well, don't revert immediately to sex that focuses on erection and ejaculation. Avoid anonymous and quickie sex. It's not likely to work for you, at least not right now.

Impotence can be very disheartening. If this program doesn't work for you, you may just need more professional encouragement and advice. It may be difficult to think about going to a sex therapist, but surely the long-term rewards are worth it. (See also *Surrogate; Therapy.*)

INFANTILISM. (Sexual pleasure associated with acting like an infant, wearing baby clothes, or using objects associated with babies.)

Some fetishes — leather, big cocks, jockey shorts — seem to be accepted and talked about even by men who don't personally share them. Others remain taboo territory. Infantilism falls into this second category, yet it's shared by more men than would care to admit it.

Infantilism can take several forms. Some men like the sense of surrendering control that comes with acting like an infant. Others are actively drawn to baby rattles, teething rings, diapers, and other baby paraphernalia, and use it while masturbating.

A few men who are into baby fantasies buy their supplies at the nearest store, keep everything in plain sight, and don't care who knows about their fetish. Until the world becomes a less judgmental place, however, most people with unusual sexual interests prefer discretion. There's no reason not to buy your toys and equipment at local department stores and baby stores; you can get adult diapers at a drugstore. People who don't know you will assume you're a father; those who do, will assume you're buying things for friends or relatives. But if you're worried that your secret will get out, do your shopping out of town.

For most people whose sexual interests fall out of the mainstream, the biggest problem is finding interested partners. Fortunately, there are newsletters and clubs for almost every special interest, including this one, which will be invaluable in helping you make contacts. See *Special Interests.*

INTERCOURSE. In a sexual context, intercourse can refer to any genital contact between two or more people. The most popular types of intercourse for gay men are described in individual sections; some less common ones are briefly highlighted below.

In the activities described here, neither man ejaculates inside the other, and there is no significant risk of transmitting HIV.

Interfemoral intercourse: This involves thrusting the penis between the thighs of a partner. It can be done lying down face-to-face, or with the bottom partner on his stomach, or in a variety of standing positions. It doesn't work if the second man's thighs are too thin.

The ancient Greeks have such a reputation for enjoying anal intercourse that the terms *Greek active* and *Greek passive* today refer to partners in anal intercourse. But scholars (yes, people get paid for studying these things) believe that while anal intercourse was known in ancient Greece, the men and boys on all those pottery fragments were usually having interfemoral intercourse.

Buttockry: Rubbing the penis in the cleft of the buttocks, but without actually entering the anus. This was another activity enjoyed by the Greeks.

Armpit fucking: As the AIDS crisis worsened, gay men started looking for new sexual combinations, and this one has proven popular for occasional variety. When your arm is held close to your body, it forms a pocket into which your partner can insert his penis. As he's fucking away, you have both hands free to masturbate. You can also spread your legs, a position not available in interfemoral intercourse; some men say that this accentuates the muscular tension they need for a good orgasm.

The area behind the knee, when the leg is bent, provides a shorter but similar pocket if you're interested in experimenting further.

Foot fucking: If the soles of your feet aren't too rough, you can make a tight passage for your partner by pressing them together. A foot fetishist — and there are more than you might think — will be in heaven.

J–K

JEALOUSY. Gay men seem to be far less sexually possessive than heterosexuals or lesbians. For the 1983 study *American Couples,* several thousand couples were interviewed about their habits and attitudes. When asked if they would be bothered were their partners to have sex with someone else, only 35% of the gay men said "Yes" while three-quarters of other respondents gave that answer.

It's not hard to speculate about the reasons for this dramatic difference. Gay men come out into a subculture in which impersonal sex is readily available. Most of us have experimented with it. While it may not have suited our needs, we've learned that sex and love can, in fact, be separated. So if our lover has a brief fling on the side, we don't necessarily feel threatened.

This pattern suggests that jealousy is a behavior that we learn, and that can be unlearned. There's no easy way to unlearn it, and some highly jealous men have no desire to change. But if you find that jealousy is sowing seeds of suspicion and guilt in a relationship, it will pay to give some thought to the subject.

In fact, jealousy can stem from any number of sources, few of which are easy to defend. Most often, perhaps, jealousy represents a fear of losing a lover.

It can also be envy that someone finds your lover more attractive than they find you.

For a man reared in, or trying to copy, a macho, masculine self-image, jealousy may reflect an attitude that his lover is almost a possession, not to be enjoyed by anyone else.

Jealousy can also be seen as an element of commitment. After many years of one-night stands, Jim finally settled down with a lover. "Sure I'd like to have sex with other guys sometimes," he explains. "But Bill and I have made a commitment to each other, and monogamy is a way of expressing that commitment."

Outside relationships: An outside relationship that involves a strong emotional commitment is easily seen as a threat to an existing relationship. In the study mentioned above, only 35% of the gay men said they would be bothered were their lover to have sex with someone else, but 76% objected to "meaningful outside affairs."

The conflict between wanting the adventure and variety of outside affairs, and also wanting the security of a relationship, can be troubling. Gay men have devised many solutions. Some couples agree that sex outside the relationship is okay — "just don't tell me about it." Others accept outside affairs only if they stay casual. A minority of couples, confident that their love has strong roots, even encourage one another to become emotionally and sexually involved with others.

The options and complications can quickly become overwhelming. It's easy to understand why conventional straight society chooses to avoid the whole can of worms by insisting on monogamy — or at least the pretense of it.

JEWELRY. Jewelry that's worn during sex should be there because you decided it would add to the experience, not because you didn't bother to take it off. Chokers and gold chains around the neck are popular with many men; they draw attention to the erotic vulnerability of the neck. Bracelets are a matter of personal taste; just be sure they aren't likely to scratch. Rings usually won't be noticed unless they can scratch — or if you're into fisting, in which case they must come off. As for your watch, take it off and put it out of sight. Nobody should be keeping track of the time.

J/O CLUBS. With the advent of AIDS, a few cities have seen the birth of a new institution: the Jack-Off (J/O) Club. You pay an admission fee or purchase a membership, strip and put your clothes in a locker, then join the fun. Rules and customs vary. Most clubs will evict you for engaging in any penetrative sex, even with a condom. It goes against the spirit of the club, and it could get them closed down.

Whether you're expected to jack off only yourself, or can extend a helping hand to another man, can vary from club to club. Modesty has no real place in these clubs; if you need a towel wrapped around your waist, you've probably picked the wrong spot to go for an evening's entertainment. Clothing that serves to highlight your sexuality rather than hide it — chaps, or a jockstrap, for example — will probably be welcome. These clubs are such a new phenomenon that customs are still evolving. If you're in doubt, watch and learn, or ask whoever seems to be in charge.

So far, J/O clubs exist in only a few of the larger cities, and aren't always easy to find. Some advertise in the gay press; others only by word of mouth. (See also *J/O Party; Masturbation.*)

J/O PARTY. The private, non-commercial equivalent of the J/O club is the J/O party. It's a chance for men to enjoy hot, safe sex in a social atmosphere.

This, too, is a new phenomenon, and the structure is still evolving. Typically it starts with a small group of uninhibited friends, who rely strictly on word of mouth to expand their circle. Some groups

mail out notices of future parties. Others do it more informally — at the end of one party, plans are made for the next. Rarely will they charge admission — that could invite legal trouble of various sorts — but you may be encouraged to make a contribution to offset costs. Some J/O parties also double as fund-raisers, asking attendees for donations to a particular organization.

If you're new to the world of gay sex, you probably won't be hosting such a party soon, but you may be invited to one. Be prompt; late arrivals interrupt the momentum. The host may suggest that you undress on arrival; in other cases, at the announced party time, someone will take the initiative to strip and everyone else is expected to quickly follow suit. As the evening progresses, be considerate about keeping clean-up simple for your host. You want to be invited back, don't you?

If you're planning a party yourself, you've probably been to enough that you'll have a good idea of what makes it successful. Have a few good porn videos available. Be sure the room is adequately warm, but not too hot — as they get sexually hotter, your guests will warm up physically, too. Be sure you've got a few guys who possess enough self-confidence to break the ice and get things started.

The trend at J/O parties is to focus more on having a good time than on everybody looking like Adonises. You're likely to find older and younger men, fatter and thinner ones, at such an event. There will likely be a few that you find quite attractive — and you may also develop some appreciation for men who, in a bar, you would quickly have dismissed as "not my type." (See also *J/O Party; Masturbation.*)

KEGELS. (An exercise to strengthen the pelvic muscles, developed by and named for Dr. Arnold Kegel.)

Originally designed for women who had trouble holding in urine following childbirth, Kegel exercises were discovered to improve ejaculatory control in many men. Both men and women have reported more intense orgasms after a month or two of Kegels.

The exercise is simple, and can be done anywhere — while you're on the phone, or driving, or watching TV. The next time you're urinating, stop the flow momentarily. Notice how you're tensing a certain muscle down there? That's the muscle to exercise. It's called the pubococcygeus muscle, often referred to as the P.C. muscle.

Begin by tensing that muscle briefly, then relaxing, and repeating the process ten or fifteen times. Do this twice a day. Gradually increase the number of repetitions. When you can comfortably do it seventy times, start holding it for three seconds each time. Again, work up to the point that you can do this seventy times. Toning up the P.C. muscle can't be speeded up any more than building up your biceps, but after a month or two of daily exer-

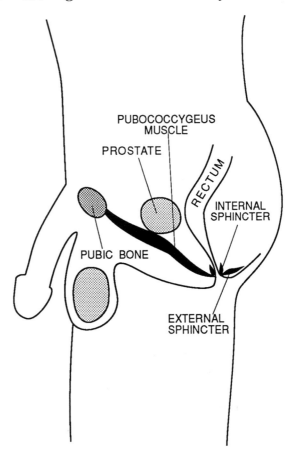

PUBOCOCCYGEUS MUSCLE

PROSTATE

RECTUM

INTERNAL SPHINCTER

PUBIC BONE

EXTERNAL SPHINCTER

cises, you should notice results. After that, you can keep the P.C. muscle in shape by just exercising it twice a week.

KISSING. Sorry, this one you can't learn from a book. Fortunately, it comes naturally. If you feel unsure, watch *Gone With the Wind,* then find someone to practice with.

Kissing needn't be confined to the mouth. You can work your way up and down a lover's body with kisses, giving him a moist and gentle kiss on the neck, then aggressively sucking on his chest and nipples, finally tonguing the base of his cock as he strokes himself.

French kissing (also known as *open-mouthed* and *deep kissing*) involves moving your tongue around in your partner's mouth, as he does likewise. You can also nibble and suck on his lips and tongue.

A word of caution about French kissing. Some people enjoy it, others don't. Many consider it quite an intimate act, and enjoy it only as a prelude or accompaniment to lovemaking. If your partner is interested, he'll already have his lips slightly open when your tongue starts to explore. Forcing your tongue through tightly closed lips is rarely a turn-on for the body attached to those lips.

Some men don't like to kiss. This may simply be a personal preference, programmed early in life like so many other aspects of sexual responsiveness. But in most cases, a man who likes sex with other men but doesn't want to kiss them is still denying his gayness. He's convinced himself that if he avoids affectionate acts such as kissing, he can have man-to-man sex without really being gay. If you get involved with a man like this, be prepared for heartache.

Hygiene: There's no bigger turnoff than kissing a foul-smelling mouth. That's a good reason to thoroughly brush your teeth first. Avoid garlic or heavy onion sauces at dinner unless your partner's eating them too. If you smoke, special rinses will help get rid of the odor, though you may not be completely successful. Tooth decay or other dental problems can also cause breath problems: Ask your dentist for an honest opinion of whether you have any cause for concern in this area.

Safety: Health authorities agree that AIDS is not communicated through close-mouthed kissing. They disagree about open-mouth kissing. No one is known to have ever gotten AIDS this way, but it's theoretically possible that it could happen, especially if you both have open cuts or sores in your mouths. The consensus among experts is that the risk is negligible. (See also *Risk Management.*)

L

LABELS. Gay. Straight. Bisexual. Top. Bottom. Labels get a lot of bad press. "I don't like to be pigeonholed with a label," people say.

The fact is, labels are useful. Without labels, we could end up at the Irish Parade instead of the Gay and Lesbian Parade.

Just don't let labels get the upper hand. At one point in your life, you probably assumed you were straight. That label, however unconsciously it was adopted, limited your ability to explore your attraction to other men. You may now identify as gay. That's fine, but if you find aspects of your personality that don't fit that label, it's the label that should get redefined — not your personality.

LEATHER. (A broadly defined approach to gay sexuality that highlights a sense of masculinity and may include S/M.)

Every large city has at least one leather bar. Its customers tend to include a wide spectrum of ages. Attire will include leather, denim (especially Levi's 501 jeans), and occasional metal accessories. Men into leather are often, but not always, also into S/M sex. (See also *Sadomasochism*.)

LEGAL MATTERS. In 1984, a drunk driver hit Sharon Kowalski, leaving her a quadriplegic with severe brain damage. Kowalski's parents refused to give their daughter's lover, Karen Thompson, full access to Kowalski, or input into her care. Seven years later, Thompson is still battling in court to win those rights.

As she pursues her legal fight, Thompson has also educated the gay community about the legal protections available to us. If you and a lover share the expenses and upkeep on a home, condo, or car, be sure that you also share the title to it. Sign *power of attorney* agreements, providing the authority to make decisions and sign documents for one another should one of you become incapacitated. It's important to have a will, and also a Living Will, which indicates what you want done if injury or illness leaves you unable to indicate your own desires.

Any gay bookstore will have several books that discuss these matters in more depth. A lawyer who's knowledgeable about gay concerns can draw up the appropriate documents simply and inexpensively.

LEGAL TROUBLE. Just a generation ago, many gay people perceived police entrapment as the biggest threat they faced. It was all too common for gay men to respond to a come-on by a plainclothes cop, only to suddenly have handcuffs slapped on their wrists. To avoid publicity, most of them paid a stiff fine — really nothing more than legal blackmail — rather than contest the charges. So widespread was this threat of entrapment that in 1952, when the fledgling Mattachine Society successfully challenged an entrapment arrest, its membership rapidly skyrocketed.

Although sex-related arrests are far less common than they were in the fifties, they can be just as devastating when they occur, especially to a closeted man. If you frequent tearooms or other cruising areas, carry a lawyer's phone number in your wallet. Should you be arrested, be courteous to the police but insist on speaking with your attorney before you make *any* statements about your activities. Don't agree to plead guilty until you've discussed, with a knowledgeable lawyer, the full consequences of such an action. In some states, conviction of any sex offense will put you on a list of registered sex offenders, with repercussions for years to come.

LONELINESS. We are all lonely at times. Dr. George Weinberg says it best in his classic work, *Society and the Healthy Homosexual:* "It is easy to confuse one's special condition with the deep sense of aloneness felt by every living human who reflects on his life, and about which nothing can be done. Homosexuals must not err in paying sizeable fractions of their incomes to experts in hopes of getting rid of this aloneness."

The best antidote for loneliness is not finding a lover, or a date, but in doing things that you enjoy, with other people, and through that, finding some new friends. Unfortunately, no one will ever believe this basic truth from reading it in a book. Some spend years learning it the hard way, and others never learn it at all.

LOVE. One legacy of the sixties is a wider acceptance of sex as a worthwhile pursuit in its own right, rather than insisting that sex always be a by-product of love.

Gay people had long known this, of course. For that matter, straight people had too; they just hadn't said so publicly.

If you're new to gay life, the dichotomy may still give you trouble. You may be comfortable with the thought of having sex with another man, but unable to accept the notion of loving a man. Or you may want to fall in love with a man, but still be uncomfortable with the thought of sex together.

Relax. Most men, when they come out, go through a period of adjustment. You could hit it lucky and immediately find your lifetime

mate. But more likely, during this period you'll have sex with several people, ranging from one-night stands to brief relationships. You'll find out more about your physical and emotional needs, and how (and where) to find the men most likely to meet those needs. You'll find out what you can offer them, and develop more confidence that, yes, you *do* have something to offer them.

You'll experience sex with love, and sex without love. You'll find that there's quite a difference. Both have their place in the world; exactly what role you want them to play in your own life is up to you. (See also *Finding a Lover*.)

LOVE AT FIRST SIGHT. If love, by your definition, involves under-standing another person as well as being attracted to him, then love at first sight is clearly impossible.

Of course, you'll hear stories to the contrary. Paul and Ralph met at a bar twenty-five years ago and, recalls Paul today, "it was love at first sight." They're still together. Their relationship sounds like quite a success story, and it is. But when pressed, Paul frankly acknow-ledges that he had that love-at-first-sight feeling "probably a few dozen times" with other men. Many of those affairs didn't even last out the weekend.

There's nothing wrong with that feeling. It's enjoyable, and psychologists have even come up with the term limerence for that swept-off-your-feet sensation. But if you assume that a relationship has to start that way, you'll miss some good opportunities that simply don't announce themselves quite so loudly.

LUBRICANT. (Any substance that reduces friction during sex.)

Most men use a lubricant when they masturbate or have sex with another man — except in the case of oral sex, when saliva is abundant. There are plenty of lubricants to choose from. Each type has its own characteristics; eventually you'll discover what feels best to you. Preferences about lubricants are less strong than preferences for certain sex acts, though, and most men can be happy with whatever's at hand.

It's best to use lubricant that comes from a tube or squeeze bottle. Anything in a tub or jar easily becomes a repository for germs, as your fingers dip in and out.

Lubricants and condoms: For the most part, the lubricant you choose is strictly a personal choice. However, if you're using a lubricant with a condom, use one that's water-based. Oil and petroleum products will weaken a condom, and increase the chance of breakage. Some of the most popular lubricants are listed below; when you're using a condom, use only those lubricants that are identified as "water-based." For brands not included here, read the label carefully; if it's water-based, it will usually say so. ("Water-soluble" is *not* the same as "water-based," and should not be used.)

Saliva. It's the default choice for oral sex, and some men like the feel of it for masturbation. For anal intercourse, get something more substantial.

KY. Originally intended as a sexual lubricant for women, KY is also used by doctors for rectal examinations, and, increasingly, by anyone having sex with a condom. It's the only lubricant that Ted and Andrew ever use. Like other water-based lubricants, KY dries out during use: at first it develops a tackiness that can provide a different and pleasant sensation; then it becomes so dry that it needs to be refreshed with water or saliva, or just squirt on some more. KY is readily available in drugstores, usually in the feminine hygiene section.

ForPlay, etc. Several brands of lubricant made specifically for sex are marketed mainly through gay channels and adult bookstores. ForPlay and Probe, which are both water-based, are widely available. Other brands come and go; before trying something new with a condom, read the package carefully to be sure it's water-based.

Petroleum jelly (Vaseline). Once the most popular lubricant for fucking, petroleum jelly (of which Vaseline is the best-known brand) is not water-based and should not be used with condoms. Because it doesn't dry out, it's still great for other activities such as masturbation and frottage.

Vegetable shortening (Crisco). In pre-AIDS times, Crisco boasted a loyal following. It's not water-based, of course, so it's not compatible with condom use, and it doesn't wash off easily, so in most gay households, it's now strictly for pie crusts.

Hand lotions. Hand lotions usually contain oils and shouldn't be used with condoms. They're fine for masturbation and frottage. Jeff reports that he likes Vaseline Intensive Care, while his lover James prefers regular Vaseline when they masturbate together. Jeff explained, "It seems silly having two types of lube, sort of like having two brands of toothpaste. But we both developed a sort of brand loyalty before we met, and we've stuck with it. I like the fact that Intensive Care just seems to dry up and disappear when you're done. James thinks it dries out too fast. But when we fuck each other's fist, we always use Vaseline Jelly, which has just the right consistency."

Soap. Soap feels slippery at first. Some soaps, however, contain minute particles that are helpful when you're getting clean, but not so good for getting down-and-dirty. Think of it as a last resort for masturbating. Soap is not advisable for anal use. While it's not likely to do real harm, it may later cause discomfort or diarrhea.

Specialty sex lubricants. You can buy a wide range of lubricants, often colored and flavored, in sex shops. Like all gimmicks, they may be fun briefly, but the novelty usually wears off soon. (The artificial dyes may be slower to wear off.) Be wary of unknown manufacturers that claim their product is "water-based." Probably it is, but there's nothing to keep them from lying if it helps sales.

M

MAIL. A wide variety of sex-related devices, videos, and publications are available by mail. For the most part, the same precautions apply here as to anything that you order by mail:

- You're safest ordering from advertisements in established magazines; while these magazines don't screen their mail-order advertisers, they won't keep running ads for a company that generates more than its share of complaints.
- Avoid ads that make extravagant claims of any sort.
- It's better to order by credit card than with a check or money order, because you'll have more recourse if the order is never filled or the merchandise was misrepresented.

Never respond to any ads for erotic material that features males under the age of consent. (Of course, the ad won't be phrased this way, but even a term like "teenage boys" should alert you to possible danger.) The government has tried, and continues to try, to entrap men with such ads. Using the U.S. mails to solicit or send photos of individuals under eighteen engaging in sex (including masturbation) is a federal crime, and is a highly risky activity. Government agents have posed as individuals, and as businesses, in an effort to make arrests. Don't become one of their victims.

MALE RAPE. See *Rape.*

MAN/BOY LOVE. See *Pedophilia.*

MASSAGE. Rubbing and kneading the body, especially in muscular areas, eases tension. Massage can also have a sexual goal, and sometimes the first type will lead to the second.

You'll be able to give enjoyable massages after reading and practicing the basic techniques outlined here. If you want to get better, you can get further guidance from how-to books, at adult-education classes, or just by paying attention as you're massaged by a professional.

First, focus on the mood and setting. Unplug the phone and turn off the television. Dim the lights, and be sure the room is comfortably warm. Candles and soothing music can also set a proper mood.

Massage oil isn't necessary, but helps. Don't pour it on directly; warm a little in your hand first. Better yet, put the bottle in a bowl of

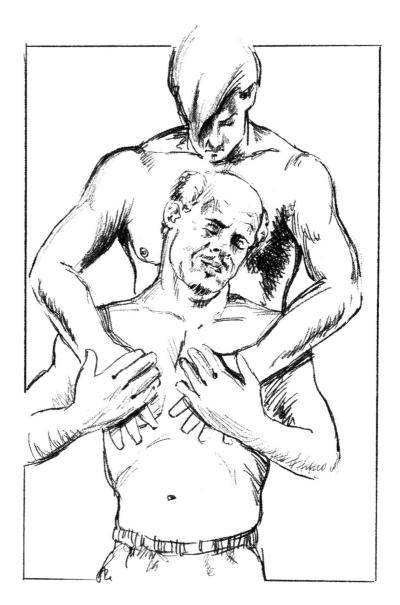

hot water half an hour before you start. Massage oil comes in a wide range of scents, as well as unscented.

The person receiving the massage should ideally be naked, but if that's going to cause embarrassment or distractions, he can leave on his briefs. Massaging consists of not just rubbing the skin, but also gently kneading the muscles below. Roll the skin and underlying tissue, when you can, between thumb and fingers.

Start with his back, working it with both hands. A lot of tension is stored here, and this will quickly relax your subject. Don't miss the small of the back and the upper buttocks, which are especially sensitive. Then move to the neck, each arm, the hands, the legs, feet, and the chest. Try to visualize where each muscle is, and give it your full attention before moving on to the next.

You can help initially relax each area by rapping it with the edges of your extended hands, quickly alternating them, as if your hands were knife blades tenderizing a steak.

Finally, if you want to end a comforting massage with some hot sex, move to his genitals.

You'll need to communicate as you go. He should tell you what feels best, when he needs more pressure, and when it's too much. The back can take far more pressure than the stomach and chest. If he's thoughtful he'll occasionally moan happily, to underscore his appreciation.

There's a hidden benefit to all this. Many of us hesitate to clearly tell our partner what we want during sex. We need a bit more pressure here or there, or a shift in focus, but we're uncomfortable saying so. The communication skills you learn during massage can carry over into sex.

MASTURBATION. (Sexual stimulation with the hand, or occasionally involving another object. Masturbation can be done alone or with a partner. Such slang terms as *beating off, jerking off,* and *jacking off* all have a similar meaning, but with a clear emphasis on using the hand to achieve orgasm.)

There seems no doubt that masturbation has been common in all times and cultures, though some have been far more open about it than others. Artwork from such varied sources as ancient Greece, Persia, Arabia, India, Japan, and native American cultures depicts men quite unabashedly masturbating.

Our own culture has been less fortunate. In the nineteenth century, scientists, physicians, and preachers joined forces to condemn "self-pollution." Their crusade had a lasting influence. As recently as the 1920s, medical students learned that masturbation caused boys to become dishonest, unreliable, and physically weak. (Today's trivia: Graham crackers were originally hawked, though in less graphic terms, as a health food that would keep boys from beating off so much.)

The famous Kinsey Report, in 1948, demolished these myths. Alfred Kinsey found that 92% of his male subjects had masturbated, and none had gone blind as a result. It's a common practice for people in relationships, as well as for those without other sexual outlets. Although today's sexperts consider masturbation a healthy and enjoyable sexual outlet, we're still influenced by writers, priests, parents, and others who grew up in a more rigid atmosphere. It will take several more generations before these centuries of propaganda have thoroughly faded.

That influence is still apparent in modern books stating that masturbation is fine "as long as you don't do it to excess." What are these writers afraid of? If you really masturbate to excess, you won't

104 ❖ MASTURBATION.

need a book to tell you to stop: Your body will send out a perfectly clear message that *that's enough*. Short of that, unless you masturbate so much that you can't hold down a job, there's really nothing to worry about.

Some men discover masturbation independently, others learn about it from friends or books. Each of us develops our own favorite methods, and it's a safe bet that someone has masturbated in every position into which it's possible to contort the human body. Among the more popular arrangements:

Prone, face up. Lie in bed or on another comfortable surface. Some men enjoy the tension created in their thighs when they bring their feet up towards them, while keeping the knees down, as they masturbate. A popular variation is to elevate the hips with a pillow.

Prone, legs above head. This position, which is popular for anal intercourse, also works for solo masturbation, especially if you're using a dildo. Simply lie in bed and swing your legs up and back. If that gets tiring you can put your legs against the wall, walking them up as high as you like.

Prone, face down. Put a towel down to protect the sheets, then lie down and pump your cock into your lubricated fist, or against a smooth cloth that you've put over the towel. The pelvic thrusting in this position provides a pleasant alternative to other positions, where most of the motion comes from your hand.

Kneeling. Kneel on a soft surface, and lean back. As you lean back farther, your thigh and abdominal muscles will tighten. For some men, this intensifies both erections and orgasms.

Standing. Sometimes there's just no time to get undressed or no space to lie down. Or you may prefer the freedom of pelvic motion that you get when you're standing. It's easier to watch yourself in the mirror in this position.

Experimenting: Masturbation provides a safe context in which to try out new sensations. Most men develop a preferred way of masturbating, one that brings the strongest possible sensations. Usually this involves applying some lubricant, wrapping one or both fists around the erect penis, and stroking up and down. But don't limit yourself to the same hand, the same lubricant, the same rhythm, and the same position every time. Vary it. You may discover something that feels even better.

Some men learned to masturbate by lying face down in bed and thrusting against the sheets, and still prefer this. If that's what you do, try manual masturbation instead sometime, and vice versa.

If you sometimes have trouble reaching orgasm with a partner, there's another incentive for varying your masturbation techniques. As your body learns that several different sensations can all lead to orgasm, you're more likely to respond to your partner's stimulation.

Jerk-off sessions also provide a good opportunity to experiment with condoms, dildos, cock rings, tit clamps, and anything else that intrigues you.

Making time for yourself: Often, masturbation is a spur-of-the-moment act to relieve loneliness, boredom, or just plain horniness. That's fine. Those things all need to be relieved from time to time.

But if you'll occasionally look on masturbation as a date with yourself, you'll find it becomes a different experience. Schedule an evening alone, a few days or a week from now. Plan for it: some music, candlelight, a special scented oil, perhaps an accessory or a new toy that you've wanted to try out, or a video with your favorite actor. When the evening comes, take the phone off the hook, and allow yourself to relax and get into the mood. You've worked hard all week, you've earned this. Take your time.

MIRRORS. Not everyone wants to invest in making their bedroom a pleasure palace. But for gay men, who sometimes end up in positions that don't include face-to-face contact, one or two large mirrors on the wall or ceiling add a dramatic visual element to the evening. "Maybe I'm just kind of narcissistic," says Jason, "but my favorite sex is when we throw some cushions on the floor in front of our full-length mirror, and Phillip sucks me off. I love watching my cock go in and out of his mouth. I like watching him fuck me, too, seeing his butt muscles clench and thrust. It's a lot more exciting than watching somebody else's porn video." (See also *Exhibitionism.*)

MONEY. Maybe you have it, maybe you don't. Being too poor to afford the essentials of life will interfere with happiness. But once you're above that level, money and happiness have little connection.

If you're on a tight budget, don't spend beyond your means just to impress a new acquaintance. Should the relationship last, he's going to learn the truth soon enough, and he'll wonder why you were so anxious to hide it. If it doesn't last — well, you'll have wasted money that you couldn't afford to waste.

If you're well-to-do, avoid the impulse to always pick up the tab and to constantly buy things for your date or lover. Let him treat you to dinner sometimes, even if it means going to Burger King or letting him cook at home. In long-term relationships, large income discrepancies can feed resentment. Phillip and Jason have resolved this by alternating such things as vacations and dinners. One time Phillip, whose income is considerably higher, decides where to go and he pays for it; the next time, Jason does. They do this for little things like dinners, and for big expenses, like vacations. Of their last two vaca-

tions, one involved flying to southern Italy for a week; the other was a camping trip in Yosemite, just a half-day drive from where they live. If anything, it's the Yosemite trip that they enjoyed most.

This doesn't mean the wealthier partner should never be generous with his money. The more you feel you're making a lifetime commitment to one another, the more you'll recognize that each man may best contribute to the relationship in different ways. There's nothing wrong with a well-to-do man helping his lover get a better education, or funding him to start a new business. But do so with open eyes. A relationship that seems as solid as granite today can crack right down the middle next year. If that happens, are those checks you signed going to be considered a gift, or a loan?

In some relationships the less monied partner (usually the younger one) sticks around only because of the money and gifts being showered on him. These are really business relationships, and while they may fill a need in the world, they have little to do with love.

MULTIPLE ORGASMS. Many women experience multiple orgasms in a short period of time. Not so with men, who experience a refractory period after an orgasm, during which they lose their erection and have no desire to get it back. This period can last as briefly as a few minutes (usually for teenagers) to quite a few hours.

Most men can have two or even three orgasms in an evening, as long as they rely on their most reliable method (usually masturbation) for the second and third ones. But gay couples don't often do that. Usually they just try to prolong the pleasurable period before the first orgasm. After both partners have come, rarely does either one feel an urge for more activity.

MUTUAL MASTURBATION. (Masturbating with a partner. Each person can be masturbating himself most of the time, or jerking off his partner. Mutual masturbation is often an end in itself, but can also accompany other forms of sex.)

Even before the AIDS crisis, mutual masturbation was popular. Half the gay men responding to a 1976 survey indicated that sex with a partner "very frequently" involved masturbating to orgasm. In today's AIDS-conscious world, this essentially risk-free activity is even more popular.

Technically, masturbating with a partner is no different from doing it alone. However, most of us grew up with the message that masturbation is wrong, or that it's anti-social, or that it's okay but only if you do it in private. It's natural, given that conditioning, to feel uncomfortable the first time you jerk off in front of a partner. Happily, once you get started, this very sense of invaded privacy can give a special charge to your session.

Being masturbated by a partner is different from doing it alone. As Jeff explains, "When it's my hand and my dick, I'm completely in control. I know just what feels best, and that's nice — but for some reason, I like it better when James is jacking me off. Sex shouldn't be about being in control, it should be about giving up control. With his hand wrapped around my cock, I really let loose. That's when I get my most intense orgasms."

You no longer have the instant feedback. You can communicate, through words or moans, what you do and don't like, but don't expect your lover to instantly and perfectly understand what you want. This sharing of control adds an element of spice to jerking off with a partner.

When you're masturbating someone else, you'll naturally start

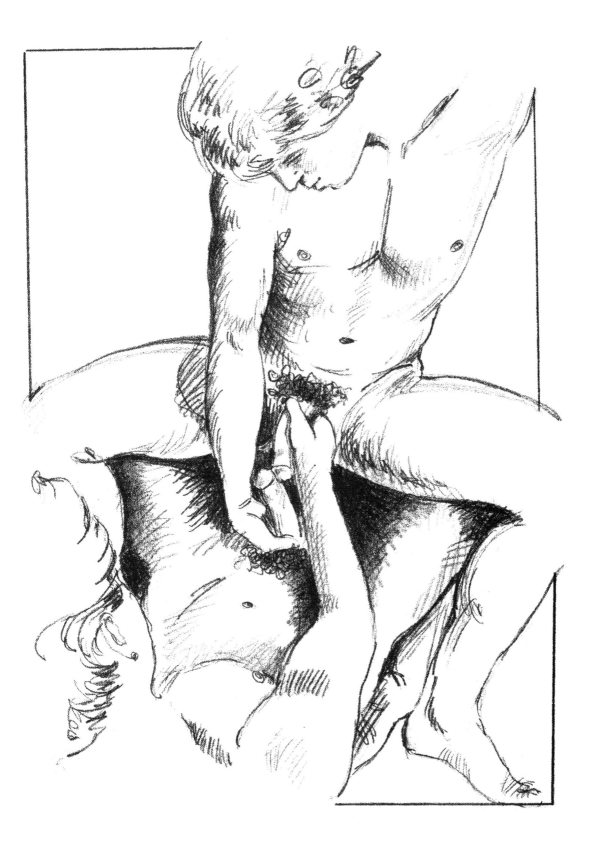

by providing the same stimulation for him that works best for you. But he's not you, so be aware of the signals he sends. Watch as he masturbates himself. How fast does he move his hand? How much pressure does he seem to apply? How does all this change as he starts to come?

If you prefer to learn by experience, here's an enjoyable approach: Lie on your back, and have your partner lie on top of you, also facing up, so that you can reach his cock as if it were your own. (If he's too heavy or too big for this to work, other positions work nearly as well.) Now begin jerking him off as he provides continual feedback: *slower, push down gently on my balls, not so much, that's right, loosen your hand a bit when it slides down, squeeze a little more when you pull up on the head of my dick, ooh, perfect, keep going just like that, more lube, a little faster now, oh, you're great, that's right, that's right...* Gee, that was a fun exercise, wasn't it?

Safety: When it comes to prevention of disease, including AIDS, mutual masturbation is as safe as you can get. There is a small theoretical possibility of transmitting HIV if your semen lands on a cut or open sore on your partner's skin, or on any other spot (his eye, the tip of his penis) where it could ultimately get into his bloodstream. In reality, no one ever seems to have been infected via this route. You're more likely to be killed by an earthquake.

N-O

NEGOTIATING SAFER SEX. See *Safer Sex.*

NIBBLING. Only a fine line separates erotic stimulation and pain, as any S/M practitioner can tell you. For most men, the sensation of having their ears, nipples, toes, neck and shoulder, or buttocks nibbled or lightly bitten by a partner stays well on the erotic side of the dividing line.

NIPPLES. (On men, the small, dark, round area of skin on the chest. Also known as *tits,* especially in the context of *tit clamps.*)

It's no longer a secret that male nipples are an erotic zone. During sexual excitement they receive an increased flow of blood and become especially sensitive. On some men they even get erect, just as the penis does, though not as conspicuously.

Nipple play can consist of flicking the nipples with your fingertips or tongue, pinching them, sucking them, blowing lightly on them while damp, attaching tit clamps to them, or even holding a vibrator to them. This is new territory for many men, and you may find that as you stimulate them more, your nipples will repay the attention with greater sensitivity and responsiveness.

NONOXYNOL-9. (A chemical used in birth control, and now often recommended as an aid in preventing the spread of HIV.)

Originally intended as a spermicide, for use in birth control, nonoxynol-9 has been discovered to kill HIV, the virus believed to cause AIDS. Since it's already an ingredient in many lubricants, nonoxynol-9 is readily available to gay men as an added protection against AIDS.

Nonoxynol-9 will not protect you by itself. Used in conjunction with a condom, however, it provides an extra margin of safety.

Nonoxynol-9 was originally developed and tested for vaginal use. It has not yet been fully tested for anal use. There's no evidence at this point of any hazards involved in such usage, but AIDS has opened up questions in many areas of health and sexuality that are still being investigated. If you're sexually active, get a subscription to a good gay magazine such as *The Advocate* that can keep you up to date about new developments and discoveries that affect you. (See also *Lubricants.*)

ONE-NIGHT STAND. (A one-time sexual encounter, entered with no expectation that it will evolve into anything more.)

Gay men may not have invented the one-night stand, but we certainly popularized it in the decade between the Stonewall Riots and the onset of AIDS. Today many men still thrive on one-night stands — while others have never had one, and never want to.

Etiquette: Although you may never expect to see your partner again, certain rules of etiquette have evolved to better the odds that you'll both have fond memories of the evening, regardless of whether those memories last a few hours or a lifetime.

If you're inviting him to your place, assume that he'll want to spend the night. If you can't allow that, warn him ahead of time, preferably with a reason that's unrelated to your feelings about him: "I'm a very light sleeper," or "I have to get up very early, so you won't be able to stay over."

Likewise, if you're accepting an invitation, let your partner know ahead of time if you won't be spending the night. To make such an announcement after you've had sex will imply that he was somehow unsatisfactory. Whether that's true or not, you don't plan to see him again, so why make an issue of it?

If you like only one activity in bed, make sure he knows that before you head home together; otherwise, you're asking for disappointment. Once things have started, don't roll over and fall asleep until you've both had a chance to come. The only exception is if he assures you that for some reason he isn't going to. If he seems to mean it — well, at this point he knows himself better than you do.

Most men with whom you have a one-night stand will view it the same way as you do. But occasionally someone who's very inexperienced or very desperate to be in a relationship will view this as the start of a lifelong relationship. As soon as you realize your differing expectations, be clear, but gentle, about clarifying your own position.

Safer sex: If you've just met a man, it's impossible to be sure that he isn't infected with HIV. However healthy he looks, whatever he tells you, even if he pulls out a hospital form showing he just tested negative for HIV antibodies, you can't even be moderately certain. Nor can he be sure of your status.

And that's okay. Contrary to what some AIDS literature tells you, there's nothing automatically risky about having sex with many different men. You just have to be careful to understand and follow the safer-sex guidelines outlined in this book. To regularly have one-night stands that involve high-risk sex (like getting fucked without a condom) is nothing more than Russian roulette. Sooner or later, the gun's chamber will be full.

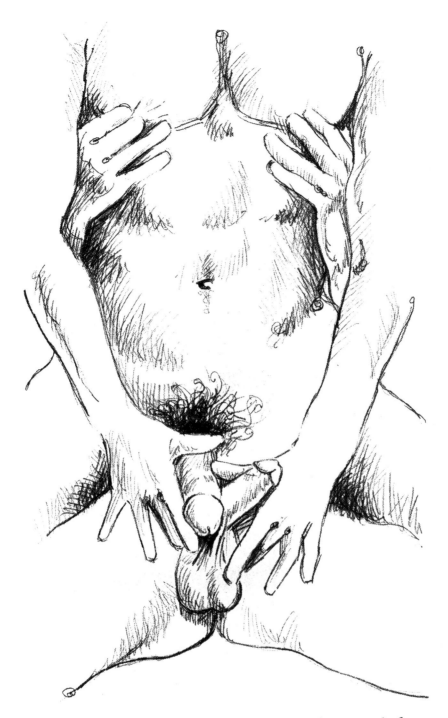

It's best to raise this issue with a potential partner before you head home together. Either he'll feel the same way, and will be relieved that you brought it up — or he'll indicate that he doesn't agree, and you can say good-bye while the night is still relatively young.

But if you don't discover your different attitudes about safer sex until you're in bed, he's the one at fault. If he wanted you to risk your life by coming home with him, he should have said so earlier. Stick to your guns. If he won't budge, then it's time to admit that you've discovered one of life's anomalies: the cad who can charm you right out of your pants. Pull those pants back on and walk out. (See also *Casual Sex*.)

OPENING LINE. (A brief comment or question directed at a stranger, with the intent of initiating a conversation — or more.)

The best opening lines will derive from the situation at hand, rather than from a book. But don't worry about it too much. Even the most cliched line will start the ball rolling with a man who's interested, and if he's not interested, it hardly matters how clever you sound.

Ideally, ask a question that invites more than a brief response. "Do you have the time?" is easy to ask, but a shy man may find it awkward to do more than just give you the reading off his watch — and he may be unsure whether you want more.

You're also better off saying something positive, or at least neutral. "Isn't this a stinky bar?" will at best peg you as a depressing person. At worst, you'll find that you're talking to the bar owner.

The suggestions below win no prizes for originality, but that can come later in the evening. These are only meant to get you started. Adapt them to fit the situation, and your personality.

At the bar:
- "Come here often?" Opening lines are usually cliches, and that's fine. This one, however, is *so* cliched that if you must use it, say it light-heartedly. God forbid he should believe that you think you're being original.
- "Hi, my name's Jack." If you've made eye contact and you think he's interested in you, why not be polite but direct?
- "Can I buy you a drink?"
- "I saw you across the room and I thought you looked interesting."
- "How do you like the music?"
- "I saw you dancing out there. You're pretty good."
- "Weren't you here with George Bradley last week?" It matters not one whit whether you really think he was, or even whether George Bradley exists.

At the gym:
- "Can you give me a spot on the free weights?"
- "Do you know how this Nautilus machine works?"
- "I'd sure like to get biceps like yours. Can you recommend any exercises?"

In the supermarket:
- "I'm supposed to get a bunch of dill. Which one is that?"
- "That vegetable looks interesting. Have you ever tried it?"

In varied situations:
- "Hi. I'm visiting from Nevada. Can you suggest some good places to meet people?"
- "Didn't we meet at George Bradley's apartment?" What a useful fellow George Bradley is!

Responding to a line: Not everyone who wants to meet you will have read this book. Some will approach you with a yes-or-no question. It's up to you to keep things moving; don't just fire back a one-word answer. Elaborate, or ask your own question. After that, if the two of you still can't get a conversation going, forget it. The chemistry's wrong. (See also *Cruising.*)

ORAL SEX. (Sexual intercourse in which one partner sucks the penis of another. Commonly referred to as a *blow job, sucking,* getting or giving *head,* and by many other slang terms. People who get paid to study these things call it *fellatio.*)

The first rule, if you're giving a blow job, is to be careful with your teeth. What feels like a slight brush against your incisor will be a major distraction for your partner. With a little practice, you'll keep your lips curled slightly around your teeth.

You'll also, with time, overcome the tendency to gag when your partner's cock plunges into your throat. Gagging is a natural reflex, conditioned by the fact that normally you don't want something big stuck halfway down your throat. Eventually your body learns that this particular case is an exception, and it will become more accommodating. If you wear contact lenses, you've experienced a similar deconditioning process: At first it feels impossible to deliberately put something into your eye, but with time, it becomes easy. (The military once thought it could identify homosexual recruits with a "Gay Reflex Test." Men who didn't gag when a large tongue depressor was applied to the back of their mouth were presumed to be gay.)

Getting back to the bedroom: As your mouth moves up and down on your partner's cock, put your hands to use too. Your fingers can *gently* fondle his balls. Depending on the size of his cock and the capacity of your mouth, you may want to use one hand to enhance what your mouth is doing. Just wrap your fist around the base of his cock, forming a tube that acts as a continuation of your mouth.

Many guys need a firm pressure on their cocks to achieve orgasm, and at first, your mouth will wear out before your partner does. Cocksucking involves muscles that don't get much other use; with practice, you'll last longer.

As you proceed, your partner will send out clues about what feels best for him. If he starts rocking his hips, try to accompany his rhythm. Does he respond best to less pressure, or more? Does he like your

action concentrated toward the head of his cock, or at the base? Does he like you to form a seal with your lips, and literally suck, creating a vacuum? If you can't detect all this from the intensity of his moans, don't be afraid to ask, "How do you like this?" as you try something different.

Your natural saliva will provide plenty of lubrication for oral sex. Sex shops sell flavored lubricants, if that appeals to you; if your partner's wearing a condom, these will mask the taste.

Men go through a *refractory phase* after they come. Your partner will quickly stop enjoying the feel of your mouth on his organ, and will become so sensitive that he doesn't want to be touched. He may reach this point immediately after orgasm, or he may want you to keep on for a couple more seconds — the timing varies slightly from one man to another. Pay attention to his signals. If he gently pushes your head back, don't dive back down for one last lick.

As for getting sucked, there's not much to be said. Enjoy it. If your partner isn't doing things the way you'd like, speak up. His mouth wouldn't be down there if he didn't want to please you. Afterward, don't roll over and fall asleep until he's gotten the attention that, by now, he's eagerly anticipating.

Positions: The man being sucked usually lies on his back. He can also kneel over his partner's chest; this works better with a few pillows behind his partner's head. A standing-kneeling combination is popular with many men. Another option, in which you simultaneously suck one another, is discussed under *Sixty-Nine.*

Mouth-fucking: In most oral sex, the sucking partner controls depth and rate of penetration, while his partner lies back and enjoys it. In an alternative position, the man who's sucking lies on his back while his partner straddles him and thrusts into his mouth. Other positions will achieve the same effect; what they all have in common is that the man who's being sucked is thrusting his hips and controlling the rhythm. This type of oral sex is technically called *irrumation.*

Irrumation is less popular because the man doing the sucking can easily feel gagged, or abused. He can exercise more control by wrapping a hand around his partner's cock, allowing it into his mouth only as far as he wants it, while at the same time providing some extra stimulation for his partner.

Safety: Health experts are hotly debating whether oral sex involves a significant risk of transmitting HIV. Some health authorities have declared that as long as you don't have open cuts or sores in your mouth, sucking cock is safe. Others believe oral sex presents a small risk, and that any cock going into someone's mouth should have a

condom around it. Stopping before ejaculation will also greatly reduce the risk.

Brushing or flossing your teeth can create small cuts in your gums. If you're having oral sex without a condom, play it safe and clean your teeth afterward, not beforehand.

Until health authorities reach a consensus, you'll probably meet some men who insist on using condoms for oral sex, and others who deem it unnecessary (and we've illustrated both approaches in this section). Just where you choose to draw the line is your decision. The *Risk Management* section may be helpful.

ORGASM. (The climax of a sexual experience, involving intense feelings of pleasure, a sudden release of tension, and usually accompanied by ejaculation. Commonly referred to also as *coming* — which can also refer to ejaculation — or *climaxing*.)

When you have sex, your body undergoes physical changes in response to the excitement you're feeling. An extra strong flow of blood pumps steadily into your penis, maintaining your erection. The blood flow also increases to other areas, including your testes, lips, ears, and nipples, increasing their sensitivity. Your scrotum tightens, drawing your testes closer to your body, in preparation for ejaculation. You may consciously tense some of your muscles, and others tense involuntarily.

When all these responses have reached a certain critical point, your body automatically takes over, contracting certain key muscles while releasing tension in others, resulting in ejaculation and the sensation of orgasm. It's possible to have an orgasm without ejaculating. (Some men also claim they can ejaculate without having an orgasm. This may demonstrate that the two aren't inextricably connected, but the ability to separate them seems to have little value except as a party stunt.)

Ejaculation is not the body's only response to orgasm. The nipples, chest, and face flush and become more sensitive. So too, for many men, do other extremities: the ears, lips, and even toes. For a new perspective on orgasm, try focusing on various occasions on different parts of your lover's body: his chest and nipples one time, his face another time, then just watch his buttocks thrusting forward and back, then his toes. (See also *Ejaculation; Erection; Sexual Response Cycle.*)

Intensity of orgasm: If you've never felt the earth move or seen stars flash during an orgasm, don't worry. Nobody else has either, at least not in real life, regardless of what movies and magazines may imply. For most people, orgasms range from mildly to intensely pleasurable. If you really think your experience is far milder than it is for most people, perhaps you can change it. See *Kegels* for your best bet. Or try changing the frequency with which you're having sex. If you've been ejaculating every day, perhaps your body would welcome more time between performances.

Different types of sexual activity can also result in different types of orgasm. Many people achieve their most intense orgasms by masturbating, since they know exactly what works best for them. For some men, an activity such as anal intercourse, in which they control the rhythm but not necessarily the pressure, works best. It's unlikely that you'll have your strongest orgasms when a partner controls all the stimulation — he simply isn't getting the same instant feedback that you can provide yourself. But the psychological boost of this shared experience often more than makes up for a slight decrease in intensity.

OUTDOOR SEX. There's probably no fantasy more widespread than that of making love, with someone who's truly special to you, on the beach or in a grassy meadow.

Even in this crowded world, you can still find places to fulfill that fantasy. The easiest option is to find the nearest spot where other gay men have outdoor sex. It may be a secluded area near a gay beach, or at a highway rest area. The best way to locate it is word of mouth, although occasionally gay guidebooks will have such listings. In many locales, however, you stand a very real chance of getting busted if you frequent one of these spots.

You're less likely to be interrupted if you find a secluded spot all your own. Chances are, should anyone stumble upon you by accident, they'll detour. If you're concerned about being found, pick your spot more carefully. Are you well off the traveled path? Can you see people approaching before they're likely to see you? Can you hear them from a good distance off? Dry autumn leaves are helpful in this regard.

The romantic feelings will last longer if you bring a blanket or sheet. Neither ants nor sand will improve your lovemaking.

P-Q

PEDOPHILIA. (The sexual attraction of an older person to children or adolescents.)

Pedophilia has a long history. There seems no doubt that the ancient Greeks really did enjoy pederasty as much as folklore suggests. Sex between adolescent boys and adult men — who acted as mentors — was common, while relationships between two adult men, as equals, were not.

But while the ancient Greeks were history's most celebrated pederasts, they are hardly alone. Boy-lovers were common in cultures as widespread as ancient Rome, early Islam, and Japan. Even in this century, some Pacific Islanders believe that boys can become men only by ingesting a man's semen, and adult-adolescent sex is ritualized.

Modern times: You won't find such acceptance in modern-day America. Most forms of consensual sex, including S/M, are accepted in the gay male community as the business of no one except the participants. But relationships between adults and adolescents are highly controversial within the gay male community, and bitterly condemned by society at large.

In mainstream culture, this condemnation usually stems from a general anti-sex attitude, and a belief that children are asexual. Gay men who object to man/boy love sometimes have the same reasons, but often they don't deny that boys have an interest in sex, they merely dispute whether true consent is possible between two people who differ so greatly in experience, maturity, and power.

That debate will not be resolved here. Suffice it to say that if you're attracted to adolescents, you need to give some thought to the inequalities inherent in such relationships; and to the legal risks involved.

The law: The age of consent — the age at which someone is considered old enough to agree to have sex — is set by state law. It varies greatly throughout the U.S. Some states add extra provisions: if both partners are adolescents, the age of consent is lower than if one is much older. Your local gay bookstore can probably refer you to a book that tells your state laws, or call a gay hotline. (See *Hotline.*)

Precautions: For men who are involved with partners under the legal age of consent, a member of NAMBLA (the North American Man/Boy Love Association) offers some suggestions to minimize the risk:

1. Ethical as well as legal considerations dictate that you carefully establish the wishes of your partner. Do not push him to become more involved than he wants to be.

2. Don't unnecessarily share information about your relationship, including the identity of your lover, with anyone.

3. Don't take photos of him, even in non-sexual situations. Such photos simply provide fuel for police and ambitious D.A.'s.

4. Don't record your experiences in a diary, letters, or in any other written form.

5. Avoid situations where a number of men have sex with the same boy, or group of boys, over a period of time.

6. A young partner may be uninformed about AIDS prevention, and he probably trusts you to protect him. It's your responsibility to engage only in safer sex.

7. Be especially cautious of swapping photos by mail, or putting information of any sort onto computer bulletin boards. These are often monitored by police, and it's easy to become trapped in a situation with strong evidence against you.

This may seem like a daunting list of don'ts. But many men today are languishing in prison simply because they had sex with a willing partner who was under the age of consent.

Alternatives: If you're attracted to males under the age of consent, there are ways to celebrate those feelings without risking imprisonment. You can purchase and read written fantasies and stories, or enjoy drawings or paintings, without fear; only photographs are covered by child pornography laws. You can enjoy photos and videos of males who are of legal age, but look younger. You can form friendships with other man/boy lovers and join organizations such as NAMBLA. You can form non-sexual relationships with boys, although this option isn't without risk: An irate and suspicious parent could easily cause trouble. (See also *Consent.*)

PENIS. (The primary male sex organ.)

Few people would quibble with this definition of the penis as "the primary male sex organ." This book is full of ideas about what to do with it. But that definition obscures an important point: The penis isn't your only sex organ. Many other parts of your body can provide sexual and sensual pleasure. From the robust and earthy sexuality of the anus to the delicate arousal of a sensitive nipple to the limitless imagination of the human mind, your body is ready to offer a wide array of treats. Any man who explores sex only with his cock is missing much that life has to offer.

124 ❖ PENIS.

Penis size: Probably no question is asked of gay advice columnists more often than, "How can I enlarge my cock?" The answer hasn't changed over the years. You can't. The penis is made of spongy tissue, not muscle. Unlike your biceps, exercising it won't make it bigger. Nor will any operation, and it's a good thing. If you could make yours larger — most likely through an expensive and painful operation — then so could everybody else. After everybody had a round of operations, you'd still find that some of them were bigger than you, and some were smaller.

Unfortunately, some men worry incessantly that they're too small. (And a few worry that they're too big.) Granted, there are "size queens" for whom penis size makes all the difference. They're a minority, though a vocal one. Most men, while they may find a large cock to be appealing, will be much more interested in the myriad other factors that shape a relationship between two people. Put your energies into giving yourself and your partner a good time. If, after that, it's clear that your partner is focused on your penis size, it's easier to get a new partner than a new penis. (See also *Erection; Genitals.*)

PERSONALS. (Classified ads, usually in gay or alternative newspapers, through which advertisers look for romance or sex.)

Some newspapers have built up their readership by providing page after page of personals in every issue. It's not always the local gay paper that has the most ads; in some cities, an alternative weekly got the jump on the competition and is still the best place to look. Many national magazines also run classifieds.

The routine with classifieds is simple. Individuals place an ad telling what they're after. You respond. Usually you're expected to write, enclosing a photo. Some newspapers now provide a voice-mail option: you'll need to call from a touch-tone phone, and a recorded message will tell you how to leave your message, or how to hear a message from the advertiser.

Like corporations that advertise soap or sports cars, individuals who advertise their bodies tend to exaggerate. "I've answered four ads placed by men who claim to have 'swimmer's builds,'" says Art. "None of them looked like any swimmer I ever saw." Traits like physical attractiveness and endowment lend themselves to such exaggeration; but when an advertiser states bluntly what he wants to do in bed, you can assume he's being honest.

The blind-date aspect of the personals appeals to some men with a sense of adventure. It's also popular with those whose sexual tastes are difficult to satisfy by meeting people in the usual places. Consequently, the personals brim with advertisers seeking their complement:

• Into glory holes? Your info about locales gets mine...

- Naked mud-wrestling: I'll take all comers.
- Chubby seeks chubby chaser.

If you meet someone after establishing contact through the personals, do it in the daytime or early evening, and in a public spot. This gives you a chance to get a better sense of him, while you can still make your excuses if the fit doesn't seem right.

Because advertisers pay by the word, or even by the letter, abbreviations abound. Ads conventionally start with two or three capital letters indicating sexual orientation and gender. A middle letter usually refers to race or ethnicity but there's no sure way to know whether the advertiser really thinks this is important, or is just blindly following custom. These letters are often followed by age, and sometimes by other physical characteristics. After that, anything goes. The most common abbreviations and terms are:

First letter:
    Bi=Bisexual
    D=Divorced (draw your own conclusions from the context)
    G=Gay
    M=Married (and presumably straight, unless the ad appears in
        a gay newspaper)
    S=Straight

Middle letter (in an opening set of three letters):
    B=Black
    J=Jewish
    L=Latino
    W=White

Third letter (or second, in an opening set of two):
    F=Female
    M=Male

Later in the ad:
    B&D, B/D=Bondage and discipline
    BB=Bodybuilder
    Bl/bl=blond hair, blue eyes. Other related abbreviations are
        br/br=brown hair, brown eyes; bk=black hair (or eyes);
        gr=green eyes.
    FF=Fist-fucking
    Fr, French="French" sex, i.e., oral sex. Usually this is followed by
        an abbreviation for *active* or *passive*, but these terms aren't
        used consistently. In most cases, advertisers call themselves
        active because they like to be sucked, but some think of this

as *passive* and use *active* to refer to the more physically active party — the man doing the sucking.

Gr, Greek="Greek" sex, i.e., fucking. Usually this is followed by an abbreviation for *active* (likes to fuck) or *passive* (likes to get fucked.)

Healthy, health-conscious=Only interested in safer sex. Sometimes *healthy* is used to mean HIV-negative status.

J/O=Jerk-off (masturbation or mutual masturbation)

S/M, S&M=sadomasochism

S/S=Safer sex

T/S=Transsexual

T/V=Transvestite

W/S=Watersports

Scams: It's a sad fact that we're usually at our most gullible when we're looking for love or sex. Even sadder, there are people waiting to take advantage of that gullibility. Many gay men have fallen victim to con artists — often prisoners — who first establish rapport with a respondent. They establish a plausible scenario (perhaps they need the filing fee for a court brief) and ask for a small financial favor — then more, and more, and more. "I can't believe I fell for it," is the common reaction of their victims, when the wool is finally pulled from their eyes.

Do correspond with prisoners, if you're so inclined. Prison can be a desolate place for anyone, and especially for a gay person. But separate your wallet from your heart, and keep in mind that men in prison are usually there for a reason.

PHONE SEX. See *Telephone Sex.*

POPPERS. (A drug that speeds up the heartbeat and causes both mental and physical reactions that, for many users, intensifies sex.)

Chemically, poppers consist of amyl nitrite or butyl nitrite. They've been sold under such brand names as Rush, Jac Aroma, and Locker Room. (And, indeed, they do smell like a locker room that has too many sweaty socks sitting around.) They are far less widespread now than they were in the 1970s.

The original poppers were amyl nitrite, a drug used for certain heart conditions. Because the liquid evaporates quickly, it's supplied in capsules that the user snaps open as needed — hence the name poppers. Although the Food and Drug Administration classified amyl nitrite as a prescription drug, it was still easy to get — by one count, sales were fifty times greater than what was prescribed. But when it could no longer be sold openly, manufacturers substituted another chemical, butyl nitrite, which has similar effects.

Use and effect: Poppers are sold in a liquid form, which evaporates quickly. The liquid is kept in a small bottle, and the user holds his thumb over the top, briefly releasing it to get a quick sniff.

Almost immediately, the drug relaxes the body's muscles. The blood vessels then dilate, and the user feels a rush of blood to the head. This is accompanied by a loss of inhibitions, a sense that time is slowing down, and a surge of raw animal sexuality. The change lasts less than a minute, but another sniff starts it up again.

Ironically for a drug so associated with sex, poppers dilate the blood vessels and thus make it harder to keep an erection.

Safety: Authorities differ as to the safety of poppers. It's widely agreed that they should not be used by anyone with heart problems, and that the body should have a chance to thoroughly recover between sniffs. Some doctors believe that occasional use will do no harm; others disagree. Some activists have even implicated popper use with AIDS, but so far with little evidence. In short, until more research is available, you don't know what risks you may be taking if you use poppers.

All forms of poppers are highly flammable; never smoke while using them, or open a bottle near a lit candle. They are dangerous if swallowed; butyl nitrite can be fatal if you ingest it and are not treated immediately.

Don't spill poppers on your bare skin; if you do get splashed, wash it off promptly. Should you get any in your nose or mouth, get medical help promptly. And don't even think of shooting them up; there are simpler ways to kill yourself.

Legality: Congress attempted to outlaw poppers in 1988, but manufacturers found a new formula that evaded the law. Congress then passed a more comprehensive law, which went into effect in 1991. It's too early to know just how effective the new legislation will be. You won't be able to buy the drug over the counter any more, but bottles that were stockpiled before the ban, as well as bootleg poppers, will probably circulate for many years to come.

PORNOGRAPHY. One difference between humans and animals is our imagination. We can see another person, and imagine ourselves in their place; animals apparently lack that ability. This helps explain why human cultures evolved the notion that sex should take place in private, or at least in prescribed times and places. As imaginations evolved, public sex got just too distracting.

That same imagination makes pornography enjoyable. We see other people having sex, we imagine doing the same thing ourselves, and bang — we're ready for action.

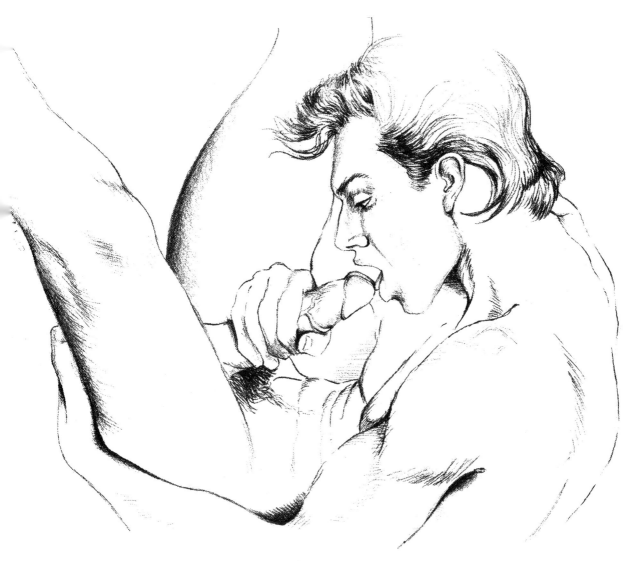

Types of pornography: Depending on just how much is left to the imagination, pornography is defined as soft-core or hard-core, terms that roughly correspond to the state of the penises involved. Hard-core porn generally depicts some actual sex.

Some men find that they're most turned on by the more explicit, hard-core pornography. Others enjoy having something left to their imagination. Men in the latter category may enjoy materials that are ostensibly produced for straight women, such as the Chippendales videos. And some gay men prefer straight or lesbian porn: "Jeff and I occasionally rent a straight S/M video," says James. "I think I get into it more than he does, but we always try to accommodate each other, and by the time the film's over, we're always both rarin' to go."

You also have several options regarding format. Some men are most readily turned on by what they see; others prefer to read, and then form their own mental images. Today's erotica breaks down into four categories:

Movies. Until the 1980s, gay porn films were just that: films. Most men went to a theater to see them. A few invested in a Super-8 projector and screen, and purchased films to show at home. But it wasn't something you did on the spur of the moment.

The video cassette recorder (VCR) has changed all that. Most gay households now have a VCR, and every town has at least one store that rents adult videos for a few bucks. You no longer need to invest heavily in equipment and a film library. Today's porn films are technically far better than those of a generation ago. In another generation, perhaps the acting will likewise improve.

Photographs and drawings. You can easily enjoy gay male photography just by purchasing a selection of the many glossy magazines that are a newsstand staple. There's a magazine for every imaginable taste. You can also purchase glossy photos from mail-order firms that advertise in these magazines, but since you can't see what you're getting in advance, there's a higher chance of disappointment.

Drawings and paintings can be lifelike — some artists who take the realistic approach work directly from photographs. Others exaggerate. Tom of Finland has made his reputation as the world's leading gay erotic artist with his drawings of the superstud with big muscles, a huge cock, and a perfectly round butt.

For a more refined approach, look in the art section of a gay bookstore.

Stories. Many porn magazines feature erotic stories as well as photos. Provided you don't expect subtlety or originality, they may be just what you're after. The 1980s also saw the proliferation of a new form of erotica: Books that simply present hundreds of erotic vignettes with titles like "I sucked off 8 marines in shower" and "Cornholed by two truckers while hitchhiking through Georgia." Classy they're not, but for thousands of men, these are the hottest thing going.

Oral. If your fourth grade teacher read a story aloud to the class after lunch each day, you may remember just how powerful the spoken word can be. As the listener, you're free to create your own images. If you're hearing a porn story, those images may be far more arousing that anything you've seen on the VCR screen. Try reading a story aloud to your lover the next time you're looking for a new kind of foreplay.

Another approach to oral pornography appears under the heading of *Telephone Sex.*

Getting your money's worth: A horny man isn't always a discriminating man, and the marketplace consequently supports some pretty badly produced porn. With books and magazines, it's easy to see what you're getting unless they're wrapped in plastic. In that case, as with videos, a smart consumer will pay attention to the producer or publisher. Learn who's producing good-quality material. If you get a video that's disappointing, try another producer next time. If it's really bad, take it back. The shop may let a regular customer exchange disappointing merchandise. There's no reason porn consumers shouldn't demand their money's worth, just as other consumers do.

With time, you'll learn which performers you prefer, as well as which producers. Joey Stefano likes to get fucked and really gets turned on by kissing; Jeff Stryker doesn't like kissing or getting fucked. Make a mental note of who gives the show that you like best.

Returning to reality: For most men, pornography is a great stimulant. It may even suggest new approaches to sex. It can reduce inhibitions, and in some cases, it's helped people deal with certain sexual dysfunctions.

It also gives a very warped view of reality. Watching Jeff Stryker on screen tells you nothing about real-life sex, just as watching John Wayne tells you nothing about real-life cowboys. We all know that porn film actors are chosen, in large part, for the size of their cocks — but that doesn't stop some men from feeling inadequate by comparison. Likewise, fuck scenes that go on forever in a movie may actually be spliced together from episodes filmed on consecutive days, or you may just be re-watching the same action from different camera angles. In short, don't feel bad if you can't last as long as the performers.

Enjoy your pornography. Just don't confuse it with reality.

Safety: Nothing epitomizes safe sex better than watching a porn film or flicking through some magazines, by yourself or with a friend, and jerking off.

The same cannot be said, unfortunately, about conditions under which pornography is produced. Many fuck scenes are filmed without condoms to protect the participants. Although the studios claim that their actors are frequently tested for HIV and other sexually transmitted diseases, that's not enough to protect the actors. It's not always possible to know, before renting a video, whether the actors will be practicing safer sex. But if more consumers would try to make such distinctions, safety conditions in these studios might improve.

PRE-EJACULATE. (Fluid that oozes from the penis during sexual excitement, but before ejaculation, also known as *pre-come.*) Before the AIDS crisis, nobody paid much attention to pre-ejaculate. A few men produced enough to serve as a handy and sexy lubricant; otherwise it was ignored.

AIDS introduced the issue of whether pre-ejaculate can transmit HIV. It's a hard question to answer: most exposure to pre-come is followed by exposure to semen. The potential hazards of the former cannot easily be separated from the proven hazards of the latter. But there's good reason to be cautious.

Pre-ejaculate *can* contain HIV. The quantities are smaller (and thus the risk is presumably a bit lower) but as a general rule: if semen shouldn't be there in a certain orifice, neither should pre-ejaculate. That means fucking without a condom is risky even if you withdraw before orgasm; pre-come still gets into the body.

PREMATURE EJACULATION. (Ejaculation that occurs before it is desired, sometimes even before intercourse begins, and often without the full sensation of orgasm.)

No one is quite sure why some men frequently experience premature ejaculation with a partner, but not when masturbating alone. One home remedy suggests "think about taking out the garbage while you're having sex." This sometimes helps, but who wants sex to be an opportunity to concentrate on housecleaning?

Certain ointments, often advertised in the tabloids, promise to prolong sex by numbing your cock, though they find a more enticing way to phrase it. The same drawback applies: why deaden your sensations for this particular experience?

Therapy: Happily, the best treatments for premature ejaculation involve *increasing,* not *decreasing,* your bodily awareness. A qualified sex therapist can probably help you. Should therapy not seem like a viable option for you, you can try any of the three self-therapy programs described below. There's no way to predict in advance what will work best for you.

Self-awareness: You may be able to gain better ejaculatory control through a three-part program:

1. Use Kegel exercises to strengthen the pelvic muscles. (See *Kegels.*)

2. Focus on the ways that your body signals that you're getting close to orgasm. You probably already recognize the "moment of inevitability," after which you're going to come no matter what you do. What sensations do you feel just before that point? What do you feel earlier? It's easiest to focus on this when you're masturbating alone, but you can also do it with a supportive partner. Men with good control have learned to interpret these signals, and subconsciously make the necessary adjustments to speed things up or slow them down.

3. Those "necessary adjustments" will vary from one man to another. For some, the area on the bottom of the penis, at the base of the head, is especially sensitive. By changing angles or reducing pressure on that area, they can keep from ejaculating. For others, tensing — or relaxing — the P.C. muscle that you learned about in your Kegel exercises makes a difference. Pay attention as you masturbate, and note how a subtle change in external stimulation, or in what you're doing internally, can affect the rate at which you approach

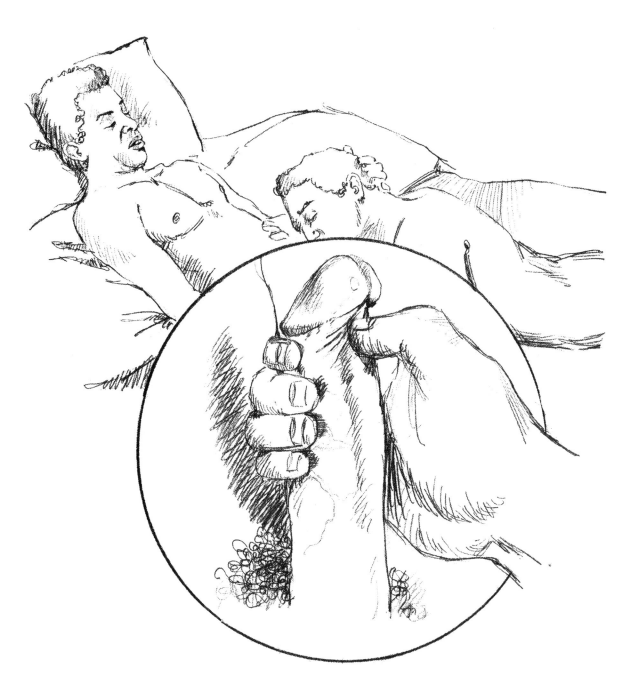

orgasm. Dr. Bernie Zilbergeld outlines a detailed program of exercises in his helpful book *Male Sexuality.*

Start-stop technique: Your goal with this program is to recognize the signals that your body sends you, and to respond in such a way as to better control your reactions. You'll go through a series of steps, gradually moving closer to that goal. You don't need to achieve perfection at each step; after you've reached the prescribed goal three or four times, you can move on to the next step.

Start by masturbating without a lubricant. Focus not on sexual fantasies, but on the sensations in your own body. When you're close to ejaculation, stop until your body has backed off. Repeat this several times, then allow yourself to come. Gradually, you'll become able to masturbate slightly longer between pauses. Your goal is to last for fifteen minutes of start-stop activity.

Next, do the same thing but intensify the sensations by using a lubricant. Again, try to last fifteen minutes before ejaculating.

Now see if you can control your excitement level without stopping the physical stimulation. Masturbate without lubricant, but when you feel yourself getting excited, don't stop. Instead, try to alter the angle, or pressure, or rhythm, so as to lessen your excitement. You won't always succeed, but you'll learn more about what works best for you. Try to do this for fifteen minutes.

If you have a supportive partner, repeat these three steps, but have your partner masturbate you. Tell him when to stop, or how to change his rhythm or pressure.

You can now switch, if you prefer, to oral or anal sex, or to an activity such as frottage. As with the original exercises, stop if you feel you're about to climax sooner than you want to. If there's a position in which you find it especially difficult to delay orgasm, don't use that position for now.

If you don't see progress after several months, it's time to try a different approach.

The squeeze technique: The steps here are similar to those above, but instead of stopping physical contact, you or your partner will use a special squeeze. When you feel you're getting ready to come, firmly squeeze the tip of your penis, just below the head, between your thumb and two fingers. After a few seconds of squeezing, the urge will subside. Repeat this four or five times, then proceed to whatever sexual activity you want.

Don't expect ingrained responses to change quickly. But if you just don't progress on your own, re-think your reasons for not getting professional therapy. Sex therapists have a high rate of success in treating premature ejaculation. It's worth investing a little time and money now, if that's the price of a more satisfying sex life for years to come.

PROMISCUITY. (See *Casual Sex.*)

PROSTATE. (A gland located inside the body, behind the penis, that secretes ejaculatory fluid and can trigger sexual excitement when rubbed. See *Genitals.* A brief discussion of prostate surgery appears under *Disabilities and special medical conditions.*)

PUBLIC SEX. The term public sex doesn't usually refer to going at it in the middle of Main Street, but rather to sex in a setting where an unsuspecting member of the public could see you.

Every medium-sized city in the United States has at least one public park where gay men cruise each other and have sex behind the bushes. Usually this activity is carried on in such a way that it's not apparent to the average nonparticipant, but if you know the score, the signs of activity are unmistakable. The easiest way to find such parks is simply by word of mouth; some gay guidebooks also list major areas. Any urban park that has a number of single males strolling about after dark is most likely a cruising area.

Approaching a man in such a spot is similar to any other type of cruising. You can be direct; you know what you're each there for. You'll find the most activity on weekends; but certain weekdays may also be busy.

Safety: Part of the thrill of such sex comes from the danger. Arrests are common, and an area that was safe a month ago may now be quite risky. In Tulsa, Oklahoma, police discovered a law in early 1991 that proclaimed stiff penalties for the felony of "sexual battery" — then defined that crime so broadly as to include the mere act of "lewdly touching" someone. Within two months, the police had arrested thirty-five men in two public parks.

Fag bashing is another danger. This, like police harassment, often comes in waves. At the very least, have a whistle handy if you head off to the park.

Other public spots: Secluded beaches and public restrooms (known in this case as tearooms) are also popular areas for public sex. The clienteles vary — beaches attract a younger crowd, eager to show off their muscles — but the approaches, and the precautions, are similar. (See *Beaches; Cruising; Tearoom.*)

R

RACIAL PREFERENCES AND RACISM. In a perfect world, we'd form friendships and relationships without regard to race. As you've noticed by now, we don't live in a perfect world.

There are those who argue that, nonetheless, we should act as if we do. That's a good goal, but probably a bit idealistic at this point in time. There are black men, for example, who sleep only with other black men because they want to channel their energy back into the black community. Given the realities of our world, that seems like an easily defended position, albeit not one that every black man will choose.

More controversial are those men who cheerfully acknowledge that they're largely turned on by men of another race. Whites who do this are frequently accused of treating their partners as sex objects. When men of color do it, they're likely to be charged with self-hatred.

The fact that such different charges are levied against whites and non-whites for the same "offense" suggests that interracial attractions are more complicated than this. No one has ever satisfactorily explained why some of us are attracted to thin blonds, others to men with muscles and moustaches. No one has even really established why some of us are gay, others straight. To suggest that most interracial affairs stem from a single motive just doesn't explain the complexities of the real world.

Interracial relationships help, in a small way, to break down some big barriers that our society has created. Couples involved in such relationships already face some major hurdles: cultural and income differences, as well as family hostility seem more prevalent in these situations than in same-race relationships. Why create another obstacle for them?

In fact, why are we so often ready to stand in judgment of one another's relationships, anyway? At the very least, those who feel impelled to make such judgments should do so only after understanding just what makes the relationship tick.

RAPE. As women have been saying for years, rape is a crime of violence and aggression that has little to do with sex. But survivors of rape find that the aftershocks can invade many areas of their lives, including sex and relationships.

The facts: Because it's underreported, no one really knows just how common rape is; statistics about male rape are even more speculative. The best estimate is that six to ten percent of all rapes consist of men attacking men. That means around 10,000 to 15,000 men are raped in the U.S. each year.

If it happens to you: Very few of these cases are reported, and while that's unfortunate, it's understandable. Too many people in our society, including many cops and judges, still feel that the victim is somehow partly at fault. But it's a rare person, man or woman, who can quickly and fully recover from the effects of a rape attack without some outside help.

Whether or not you call the police after being raped, do call a rape counseling center. They have experience with both men and women, and they can help you evaluate your options. They'll counsel you about dealing with the police, if you decide to go that route. They'll know about getting tested for possible exposure to sexually transmitted diseases, and they can steer you to a support group for men who have been raped, if one exists in your area.

REFRACTORY PERIOD. (The delay following an orgasm in a man, before another erection and orgasm are possible.)

The refractory period typically lasts anywhere from fifteen minutes to several hours in most adult men, and tends to increase with age. In adolescents, it can be so brief as to be non-existent. (See *Sexual Response Cycle.*)

REJECTION. Gay or straight, rejection is a part of life. If you approach other men for dates, dances, or sex, you're going to occasionally be rejected. The best way to deal with this is easier said than done, but it's still worth trying: Learn to take such rejections in stride, and to quickly move on. An evening at the bar in which you ask ten men to dance, and only five say yes, is still livelier than one in which you ask nobody, and nobody says yes.

Sometimes, of course, you'll be the one who gets asked. If we're just talking about a trip to the dance floor, it's a good idea to say yes, even if the invitation comes from someone who isn't your idea of Prince Charming. First, you may discover that you like him better than you originally expected. But even if that doesn't happen, why get a reputation as a snob? You can firmly but politely disconnect yourself after one dance, if you so desire. Meanwhile, perhaps Prince Charming *is* watching, and he's just getting up the nerve to ask you to dance. Observing you turn up your nose at someone else will hardly encourage him to come over and say hi.

One man who knows this well is Jim. He's in his early fifties and years of overeating, smoking, and no exercise have taken their toll. He was forever coming on to young men who appealed to him, and he was usually turned down — Jim probably got rejected in a week more than most of us do in a lifetime. But he just moved on to the next possibility, as easily as if he was asking the time. More weekends than not, someone said yes. A few years ago, one of those young men ended up staying; they've been together ever since. [Postscript: They were together when this was first written. They've since broken up. But two good years is still better than none.]

The gay male community is light-years ahead of heterosexual society when it comes to taking rejection. Rita Mae Brown once disguised herself as a man and visited a gay bathhouse in New York. What struck her most, she wrote, was that an invitation could be easily turned down, yet the rejection didn't seem to be an insult, and it wasn't misinterpreted as playing hard to get.

RETARDED EJACULATION. (The inability to reach orgasm with a partner.) Men who suffer from retarded ejaculation function fine when they're masturbating by themselves; the problem develops only with a partner. In some cases, a man can come when a partner is jerking him off, but not when he's fucking or being sucked off.

A lot of factors combine into any one sexual experience: what your boss said to you at work today, your feelings about sex, the technique your partner uses, and how you feel about your partner. Most men will, on some occasions, hit a bad combination and have difficulty reaching orgasm. But if this happens frequently or all the time, yet you have no trouble coming when you masturbate alone, then probably you want to change it.

Therapy: Retarded ejaculation usually stems from psychological factors. Most of us grew up in a homophobic and sex-negative culture. Although you may consciously feel fine about being a sexually active gay man, all those anti-sex messages have left their imprint on your psyche. Orgasms, after all, are not something that you trigger consciously.

Just as learning to ride a bike is easier with the intermediate step of training wheels, sex therapists have devised a treatment for retarded ejaculation that progresses in stages. It requires a supportive partner who understands your goals.

Start by separating yourselves enough that you can masturbate to orgasm, while he does the same. Usually, this means going into a separate room with the door closed. In extreme cases, you may need to be in a separate building, and set a time at which you're going to both masturbate. The goal is to move in small steps, from orgasms achieved in complete privacy, with no one knowing what you're doing, to those reached with — and often stimulated by — a partner.

When you can reach orgasm in this situation, then at the next session, slightly reduce the barrier between the two of you — open the door, for example. When you're comfortable with that, the next step is to communicate, by voice or by moaning, how you're each feeling.

Next, get in the same room, but with a bookcase or other barrier between you. Then remove the barrier, but face in opposite directions. Finally, you should be able to lie in bed together and watch one another masturbate. You may be able to progress from one stage to another after just one session, or it may take several weeks. Don't try to rush. If you need to, you can backtrack to a previous stage.

Once you can masturbate with your partner, side by side, everything may be solved for you. More likely, though, you'll still have difficulty achieving orgasm in response to your partner's stimulation. The principle of gradual change still applies. The next time you're having sex together, masturbate until you're close to orgasm (or even to the "moment of inevitability" when you know you're about to come), then switch to being masturbated or sucked by your partner. (This isn't a good point at which to try fucking him — you'll lose your momentum in the time it takes to enter him.) Gradually let him take over at an increasingly early point, until he can bring you to orgasm all by himself. These orgasms may not be as strong as the ones you experience by your own hand, but much of that has to do with the fact that it's still a new sensation for you.

Now that you're multi-versatile, you may find that you still prefer to masturbate with him, but at least you'll feel you're doing it out of preference, rather than necessity.

Physical factors, as well as psychological ones, probably contribute to retarded ejaculation in some men. You may simply require more pressure on your cock, in order to reach orgasm, than you'll get from oral or anal sex with most men. You may be so accustomed to a certain sensation that you achieve through masturbation that no partner is going to bring you off until he learns just what you need. The section on *Mutual Masturbation* offers suggestions about achieving this communication.

For some men, the solution is to use a vibrator when having sex with a partner. Held against the base of the penis (or wherever it feels a best), an inexpensive vibrator may induce even the shyest cock to quickly gush forth.

If it's your partner, and not you, who is experiencing retarded ejaculation, ask if he'd like to try one of the above therapies. Chances are he'll be grateful you raised the subject.

Limitations of therapy: The field of human sexuality is still poorly understood. Most cases of retarded ejaculation seem to be psychological, but there may be physical factors, as well. If you come easily during oral sex, but not when you're fucking, it may be that your body is just wired a little differently from other men. Desensitization procedures like that described above can improve your response to various types of stimulation, but if your body physically prefers one activity over another, you're unlikely to change that.

RIMMING. (Orally stimulating, exploring, and massaging a partner's anus with the tongue, scientifically known as *anilingus*.)

Rimming can be a part of foreplay, often in connection with tongue play on other parts of the body. The rimmer's tongue licks and teases the outer parts of the buttocks, slowly working toward the center, finally darting against, and even into, the anus. Often rimming serves to relax the anus, as a prelude to fucking.

Few people are neutral about rimming. Some consider it an exquisite mix of odor, taste, and feel. "It's my favorite taste treat," quips Jim, undoubtedly tongue-in-cheek. For others, it's a complete turn-off. Some enjoy rimming only if their partner is fresh from the shower; for others, that takes all the fun out of it.

Safety: In the early days of AIDS research, rimming often ended up on the "highly dangerous" list of proscribed activities. This reflected a "better safe than sorry" approach to AIDS prevention, and perhaps also the hang-ups of researchers, rather than medical fact. Rimming is now considered to present little chance (some would say no chance) of transmitting AIDS. However, it can transmit hepatitis and many intestinal parasites that, while rarely fatal, are quite unpleasant. The risks are lower for monogamous couples, but even an apparently healthy lover could be harboring a virus or bacteria, picked up non-sexually, that can infect you. (See *Sexually Transmitted Diseases*.)

You can take most risk out of rimming by using dental dams.

RISK MANAGEMENT. AIDS educators frequently divide all sexual activities into three categories: High risk (anal intercourse without a condom); Low risk (oral sex, anal intercourse with a condom); and Safe (mutual masturbation). They urge all gay men to restrict themselves to activities in the last category.

That's fine if you must condense our knowledge of AIDS into a few sentences. But it distorts reality. A few AIDS educators now advocate that we think in terms of *risk management* — understanding all the factors that determine the risk of a certain activity with a certain partner.

This approach is controversial. Some health officials believe that *no* risk is acceptable, and would shun the ideas listed here. But I believe that for many gay men, risk management is a sensible ap-

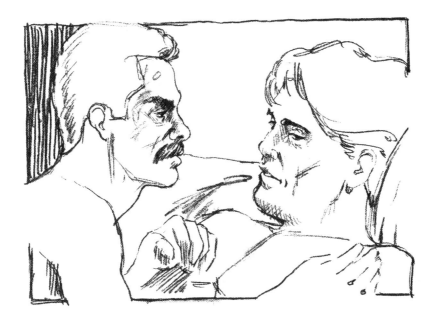

proach. Although these principles are rarely advocated in print, a great many gay men already follow them in practice.

Most researchers agree that AIDS is caused by the Human Immuno-deficiency Virus (HIV). You can get infected with this virus if fluids (such as semen or blood) from an infected person are absorbed into your body. Risk management requires that you consider four factors in evaluating the risk that you're taking. (A few AIDS activists and researchers believe AIDS is caused not by HIV, but by another yet-unknown virus or agent. However, nearly everyone agrees that whatever the cause, AIDS is spread more efficiently through some activities than others, so these guidelines still apply.)

1. Your own HIV status. Few of us can be certain that we aren't infected with HIV. In estimating the likelihood that you're not infected, look at several things.

Have you been tested for the HIV antibodies? (See *HIV Status.*) It can take months, possibly years in some cases, for these antibodies to build up. Many men, therefore, get tested twice, about a year apart. If you test negative six months after your last possible exposure to HIV, then you're likely to really be negative; two years later, and you can be virtually certain.

How many people have you had high-risk sex with? How often? Just how risky was it?

How long has it been since you had unsafe sex? AIDS has a long incubation period. You can go for ten years, probably longer, between exposure and the first symptoms. But usually some symptoms will appear much earlier.

Have you had other possible exposures? Sharing needles during

IV drug use puts you at risk. So do blood transfusions before 1985; since the middle of that year, tests have kept most contaminated blood out of the donor pool.

2. Your partner's HIV status. Your lover or partner can evaluate his own HIV status using the same criteria. The tricky part comes when he communicates that information to you. Have you known him long enough, and well enough, to completely trust him? Does he understand HIV transmission well enough to accurately assess whether he might have been infected? Are you *certain* that raging hormones aren't clouding his judgment?

This is where it's easiest to slip. You've known Randy for a month now. "I think it's time for us to drop this safer-sex crap," he says. "I know I'm not infected, and I trust you when you say you're not. Don't you trust me?" He's smart, handsome, affectionate, and the very image of health. Could he possibly be infected with AIDS? Yes, all too easily.

3. What you'd like to do together. Anal intercourse without a condom is extremely risky for the person being fucked, and involves some risk for the person fucking. With a condom, there's a small risk — condoms can break. Experts differ when it comes to oral sex. Most believe there is little or no risk in sucking up to the point of orgasm. The risk goes up slightly if he comes in your mouth, and slightly more if you swallow it. The chart here shows how AIDS educators compare the relative risks of various activities. Note that this evaluates only the risk of HIV transmission. The descriptions in this book for other activities discuss all the risks in more depth.

Also note that health professionals don't always agree. Half of those we surveyed thought that getting fisted and rimming involved no significant risk of HIV infection — the other half thought otherwise.

4. How important a particular sexual activity is to you. If you don't particularly like getting fucked anyway, then the small risk involved in anal intercourse with a condom really isn't justified. But if that activity is an important part of your sex life, you may decide the risk is acceptable.

Put it all together. Now, rather than use that simple Safe/Low risk/High risk breakdown, you can make a more knowledgeable decision. It's still tricky: You're dealing with several risk factors, but it's hard to quantify each one. No one has yet been able to say "You've got X chance of being infected if you suck off a partner who's HIV-positive, and Y chance if he fucks you." Even if we did have all these numbers, you don't want to pull out a calculator before you have sex.

Instead, you must use your judgment to decide when a certain

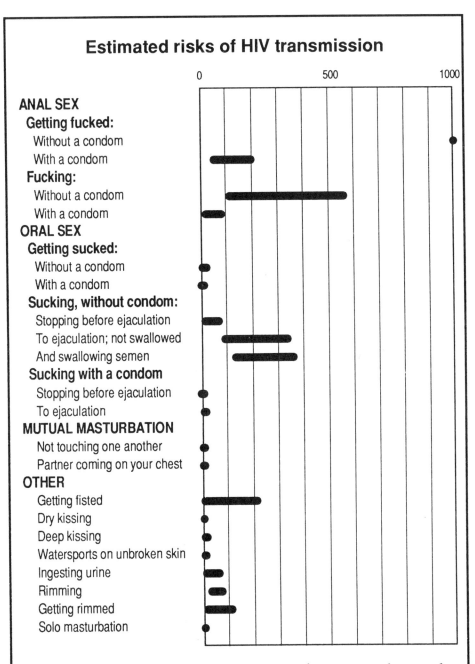

Estimated risks of HIV transmission

	0	500	1000

ANAL SEX
　Getting fucked:
　　Without a condom
　　With a condom
　Fucking:
　　Without a condom
　　With a condom
ORAL SEX
　Getting sucked:
　　Without a condom
　　With a condom
　Sucking, without condom:
　　Stopping before ejaculation
　　To ejaculation; not swallowed
　　And swallowing semen
　Sucking with a condom
　　Stopping before ejaculation
　　To ejaculation
MUTUAL MASTURBATION
　　Not touching one another
　　Partner coming on your chest
OTHER
　　Getting fisted
　　Dry kissing
　　Deep kissing
　　Watersports on unbroken skin
　　Ingesting urine
　　Rimming
　　Getting rimmed
　　Solo masturbation

Interpreting this chart: There are no scientific statistics showing the likelihood that a given activity will transmit HIV. To estimate the relative risks, we asked ten AIDS educators to rank certain activities on a scale where 0 represented risk-free solo masturbation, and 1000 represents receptive anal intercourse (getting fucked) without a condom. We then averaged the lowest half of the answers, and the highest half, and used those averages to portray an approximate range of risks. This graph represents informed opinion, not scientific fact. For a fuller description of the survey, see the Appendix.

activity with a certain partner involves too much risk. If you're reasonably sure that both you and your lover are HIV-negative, for example, you may decide that oral sex without a condom is okay — that you're willing to take the small theoretical risk involved. With a partner who's recently had high-risk sex, you might decide that oral sex is just too risky.

Other people will draw the line at a different spot. Some will decide that the risk involved in oral sex, even with someone known to be HIV-positive, is too small to worry about. What's important is that you understand the facts, and make your decision, *before* you're in bed together. Once you're horny and eager to go, it's too easy to make compromises.

A risk management approach to AIDS recognizes that we all take risks every day, whether it be driving to work on the freeway or walking home alone at night. Some of us will get hit by a drunk driver on the freeway. We'll be sorry we got into a car that morning; nonetheless, we were taking a reasonable risk. So it is with AIDS. If all of us restrict ourselves to only very low-risk activities, a few of us would still get infected, but the AIDS epidemic would soon end.

Meanwhile, if you're uncomfortable with *any* AIDS-related risk, you'll find plenty of others who feel likewise. Anyone worth having sex with will respect that.

Caution: There's a good reason so many AIDS educators don't discuss risk-management principles. Some men are so eager to dispense with condoms and safer-sex precautions that they ignore any facts that get in their way. If you think a risk-management perspective on AIDS will tempt you to take unreasonable risks, then stick with traditional wisdom and put all unsafe activities on your forbidden list.

ROLE-PLAYING. (Taking on the role of someone else, as a part of sex play.)

Some men's sex lives perk up with occasional role-playing. Typically, you and your lover will agree on your roles, set up a scenario, then play it by ear. Usually one of you, as the authority figure, will control the action. Suitable attire helps, and if you play the same roles repeatedly, perhaps outfits could go on your holiday gift list.

Provided you don't get so carried away in your role that you forget about safer sex, or actually injure one another, role-playing is perfectly safe and would be enjoyed by far more people than actually try it. Here are a few popular scenarios to get you started:

The schoolmaster and the student: The student has been sent to the office for misbehavior, and it's the schoolmaster's responsibility to administer the appropriate punishment.

ROLE-PLAYING. ❖ 145

The daddy and his son: And Junior has misbehaved.

The hustler and his john: The john is paying for this, and he's calling the shots.

Two teenagers discovering sex for the first time: Hmm, what do you think this is like? Let's try...

The cop and the criminal: The officer has just made an arrest, and on the way to the station, he detours to a deserted street. Who's going to believe the accused's story about what happened there?

The cowboy and the rustler: You've just caught a man trying to steal your horses. First you tie him to a tree. Then...

The sex researcher and his subject: All kinds of things have to be done in the name of science...

ROMANCE. Romance involves an element of mystery. Romance shouldn't ever disappear from a relationship, but it changes as two people come to know each other better. If you see this change as a failure of the relationship, you'll constantly be breaking things off because the magical romantic period is gone. Far better to look for opportunities to infuse your relationship with new experiences, to keep that spark alive.

If the romance has disappeared from your relationship, it's time to round up the usual suspects. They include:
- Taking him for granted;
- Smothering your differences;
- Losing track of your other friends and interests;
- Workaholism;
- Resentments that are allowed to smoulder;
- Letting your body go to hell;
- Unvarying sexual routines;
- Closing down communication about sexual fantasies.

RULES. Society has tried to surround sexuality with so many bogus rules, that it's tempting to do away with *all* the rules. That's too extreme. Here are a handful of rules relating to sex that I believe are worth keeping:

1. Listen to your instincts, but don't blindly obey them.

2. Welcome an opportunity to experiment with new activities if the circumstances seem right.

3. Make this an experience that will leave good memories for you, and for anyone who's with you.

4. *Before* you go out with someone, decide what your safer-sex boundaries will be. Discuss them with him before the second kiss. (Before the first kiss, you may not be sure the subject's going to come up.)

5. Don't take sex too seriously.

S

SADOMASOCHISM (S/M). The letters S/M technically stand for sadism and masochism — sexual excitement triggered by causing pain, and being subjected to pain. In the context of gay sex, however, S/M has taken on a broader definition, and refers to consensual sex that often involves dominant and submissive role-playing or physical restraint and may include the infliction of erotic pain, discomfort, bondage, punishment, or verbal humiliation. A key element of S/M is the strongly contrasting roles of the participants: one is dominant, the other is dominated. Pain isn't necessarily involved. When present, it's usually mild or moderate, and is always consensual. The goal of S/M, as of any other sexual activity, is mutual pleasure, and to emphasize this, some modern practitioners refer to it as "sensuality and mutuality."

The roles: The dominant partner is usually known as the *top, master,* or *S* (only rarely as a *sadist,* because his role is really quite different from stereotypical sadism). The submissive partner is the *bottom, slave,* or *M.*

Very occasionally, two men form a long-term relationship in which they never step out of these roles. More often, they adopt the roles only during sex. Before and after that they are equals, and the roles they adopt during sex may differ markedly from their daily real-life jobs and personalities.

In fact, just as sex can serve as an escape from problems at work, S/M roles often amplify that escape. The corporate president may relish being an M, letting someone else make all the decisions. The office gofer may welcome the chance to be in charge.

Some men take only one role: *S* or *M.* A majority will play either, though most have a preference for one or the other.

Why it's popular: Most of us have, at some point, fantasized about bondage, or other situations involving dominance and submission. S/M allows us to act on these fantasies, to see where they take us, and then to go further — or retreat. For the M, it's a chance to be safely out of control.

The roles involved in S/M offer several advantages. For a man looking for a one-night stand, having the rules spelled out in advance increases the chances of a satisfying experience. On the other hand, for partners who are familiar with one another, the roles can become liberating. If you're about to step into the role of a master — and know that you'll step out of it at the end of the night — you're empowered to explore feelings that you've previously confined.

There seems to be a physiological element to S/M, too, which is powerful but poorly understood. Several leathermen, most notably the late Geoff Mains, have theorized that pain heightens a sexual experience by triggering the release of chemical endorphins in the body. Although this theory is still controversial, some experienced S/M practitioners claim that their sexual experiences are far more intense than what they get from "vanilla" (non-S/M) sex.

Men who no longer look like a college jock find another appeal: S/M culture values maturity and experience. Men who are turned on by beards, bald heads, and beer bellies go to leather bars, not to the disco.

Getting started: An S/M novice is usually trained, in the M role, by an experienced S. You can meet a partner at a leather bar, by answering classified ads in gay papers, or through a local leather or S/M network. Talk to a man before you agree to go home with him; if your instincts tell you this isn't right, then keep looking.

In fairness to yourself and your partner, be clear that you're a novice, and express as accurately as possible what you are looking for. Make sure you both agree about safer sex, and about your limits. Establish all this before you go home together. Once you enter his bedroom or playroom, he's the boss.

The inexperienced man who wants to start in a dominant role will have more difficulty finding a partner. The S/M relationship involves a high degree of trust. The M may be tied up, strapped down, or otherwise fully dependent on the S's good faith, knowledge, and judgment. Many M's aren't about to entrust their lives to someone who doesn't know what he's doing. But some are willing to combine the roles of teacher and bottom; with a bit of looking, you may find one.

If you and another inexperienced man want to experiment with S/M together, go ahead. Just use some common sense. You can wrestle and spank each other to your heart's content and not get hurt. You can tie your partner down and jerk him off. You can administer light pain with tit clamps, clothespins, or similar apparatus. Just remember that the pain which seems erotic before orgasm will feel like pain again afterward. Be ready to remove clamps and uncomfortable bindings promptly.

Before you get into activities with an obvious potential for harm, such as whipping, torture, heavy restraints, or anything that could interfere with breathing, learn what you're doing. Knowledgeable friends and written literature will both help; see the Bibliography.

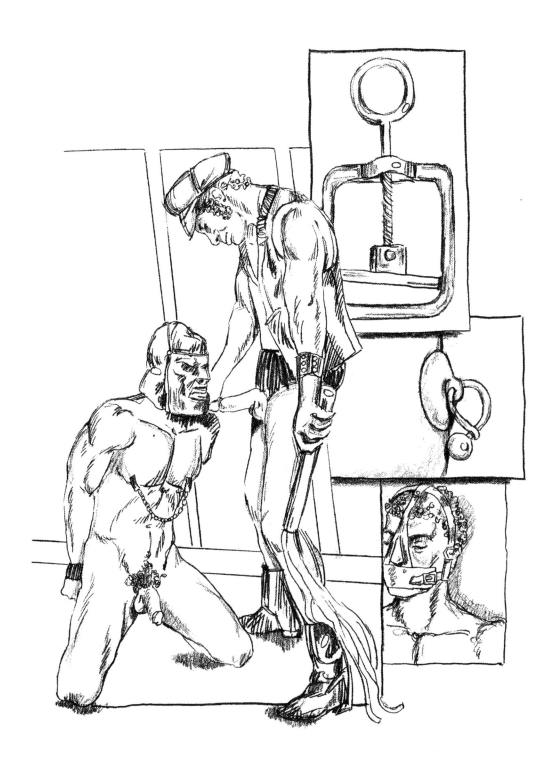

Activities: Most S/M activity falls into one of several categories. Punishment, torture, bondage, and humiliation are the most common; often they overlap. Some of these go beyond the scope of this book, but you'll find brief suggestions under *Bondage* and *Role-Playing.*

Drugs: Throughout much of the S/M community, clean and sober play is now considered the status quo. If you want to use drugs or alcohol, let your prospective partner know in advance — you may need to negotiate that, or find another partner.

There are good reasons for this: In an S/M scene, the S is like the driver of a truck. If he knows what he's doing, he and his passenger should reach their destination in good shape. It's fine for him to have a drink first, but like a truck driver, the S shouldn't try to fill his responsibilities while he's drunk or stoned.

A good S will take care of his passenger, whether the M is sober or not. But until you know your partner well enough to trust his judgment and experience, it's best for the M to be sober, as well. In any case, of course, get your master's permission before using drugs or alcohol.

We all experience a good deal of stress in our everyday life. For some of us, S/M provides an ideal release for that stress. It may not be right for you, but tastes change. Many people don't discover their attraction to S/M activity until years after they come out. You may not be into S/M now, but the fewer judgmental comments you make about it today, the smaller the chance that you'll be eating your words a decade from now. (See also *Safeword.*)

SAFER SEX. (Sex that involves no risk, or only minimal risk, of transmitting the AIDS virus.) Some authorities refer to *safe sex* rather than *safer sex.* I prefer the latter term because risk levels are a continuum, ranging from the absolute safety of mutual masturbation, to the high risk of unprotected anal intercourse, with many gradations in between.

In the early 1980s, as researchers learned more about AIDS, they realized that it could be transmitted through what they euphemistically termed "the exchange of body fluids." Fortunately, the gay press was more specific, or nobody would ever have known what the experts were talking about. HIV — the virus that most experts believe causes AIDS — is usually transmitted through blood, semen, or vaginal fluids. It may exist in saliva, sweat, tears, and urine, but there's no evidence that anyone has ever been infected by these fluids.

Negotiating safer sex: With any new partner, you must address the issue of safer sex at some point: Do you both want to practice it? And where do you draw the line? It's better to start that discussion earlier rather than later.

If you're the up-front type, you can just bluntly ask, "How do you feel about safer sex?" But some of us have trouble being that direct, and other approaches work just as well. Bring up the general subject of AIDS — a recent TV program or newspaper story can be a good way

to get started. Then channel the conversation in a more personal direction, so you can give your own views. That invites him to discuss his feelings, but even if he doesn't, he'll at least know how you feel.

The odds are, he'll be glad you brought the subject up. With luck, you'll see eye-to-eye and have smooth sailing ahead. But even if that's not the case — if you want to practice safer sex and he doesn't — you'll both be glad you discovered your differences promptly.

When it's not necessary: You don't need to use safer sex if you're certain that neither you nor your partner is infected with HIV. Although some magazine articles and TV shows have counselled the public to "always use a condom," you simply can't get AIDS from someone who's not infected. The catch, of course, is that rarely can you and your partner each be sure of the other's status.

Discussion about this subject should take place while you're both sober, and well before you get in bed together. A throbbing hard-on can spoil anybody's judgment. A longer look at the issues involved in safer sex appears under the heading *Risk Management*. (See also *AIDS; Condoms; Dental Dams; Nonoxynol-9,* and see specific activities for a discussion of their health implications, especially *Anal Intercourse; Fisting; Frottage; Intercourse; J/O Clubs; J/O Parties; Kissing; Mutual Masturbation; Oral Sex; Rimming.)*

SAFEWORD. (A word or other signal, used when role-playing, that stops the action.)

Part of the enjoyment of S/M and other role-playing comes from the freedom to fully explore your chosen role. If a Master is whipping you, your role may demand that you beg him to stop. How can he know whether you're just playing your role, or whether you really can't take it any more?

The answer is a safeword. This word, established in advance by both parties, communicates, "This is going too far. I want us to both get out of our roles and stop, right now."

A safeword should be easy to remember. Don't select a word that's likely to be used in the normal course of a session. "Stop" and "ouch" are poor safewords. On the other hand, don't pick one that's too odd. Even if it's never used, having the safeword "rutabaga" floating in the background would put a damper on most scenes.

This still leaves lots of options. One popular choice is to use your own name. That's easy to remember, and only the most extreme narcissist would blurt it out accidentally. In group S/M scenes, the preferred safeword is often, quite simply, "safeword."

If you're gagged, you'll need a signal rather than a safeword. Don't rely on a signal that's easily missed, like wiggling a finger. The movement of an entire arm or leg, or of your head, will attract attention faster.

A dominant partner who ignores a safeword is dangerous. Find another partner. Likewise, someone who uses a safeword too freely won't be invited back to play again.

SCAT. (The use of feces as a source of sexual excitement; this penchant is more technically known as *scatology* or *coprophilia.)*

References to scat have appeared here and there through the

ages. Several Taoist writings from seventeenth-century China include it, and a century later, the Marquis de Sade was writing pornography about coprophilia. At no time, however, does it seem to have been widely popular, and today it's very much a minority taste among both gay and straight populations.

Scat may involve smearing feces on oneself or a partner; or actually swallowing a partner's shit. The former activity involves relatively little health risk, provided it's done on unbroken skin. Ingesting feces, even those of an apparently healthy person, can result in a wide range of complications including hepatitis, intestinal parasites, and toxic poisoning. There are good reasons why this activity has never been popular.

SCENTS. In the animal kingdom, odors play a dominant role in sex. Just watch a couple of dogs as they sniff each other's crotch to find out what's up.

Humans rely more on sight. But we still respond powerfully to the right scent, and those who ignore this aspect of sexuality are missing out.

The most common scents occur naturally: a hot body on a warm day, a smelly armpit or crotch, the jockstrap from yesterday's workout, the odor of cock cheese on an uncircumcised penis. Not everyone is turned on by these, and some men find them appealing only in moderation, but they're free, and easy to come by, and shouldn't be overlooked.

At the other end of the respectability scale are scents that come in bottles: colognes and after-shaves. Even if you don't wear scents during the day, you can dab a little on for the evening. The woodsy odors make a more conscious impression, while a faint musk sense goes straight to the subconscious. Use them cautiously at first, and experiment with different brands until you find just what you like. More importantly, try to find out what appeals to the man you're interested in — on this score, you'll learn more from his instinctive response than by asking "Do you like my cologne?"

SEDUCTION. Sometimes you're interested, and you think he's interested, and you just need to nudge things along.

There's no single way to seduce a man. Much depends on what feels natural for you, and what seems right for him. The traditional techniques are still effective: A pleasant dinner that's not too heavy. Soft music. A glass of wine. Candlelight. (If lighting candles seems too self-conscious, you can light them ahead of time while the room is brighter. When the sun goes down and you dim the lights later, the candles will gently add their own touch.)

You can try less subtle approaches if the evening wears on too slowly: "A friend gave me a new male video for my birthday. I haven't seen it yet. Want to watch it with me?"

Don't overdo your planning. Don't set the lubricant, condoms, and towels on the pillow, or even next to the bed. Use a nearby bureau drawer. Nobody wants to feel that his interest was assumed all along — even if it was.

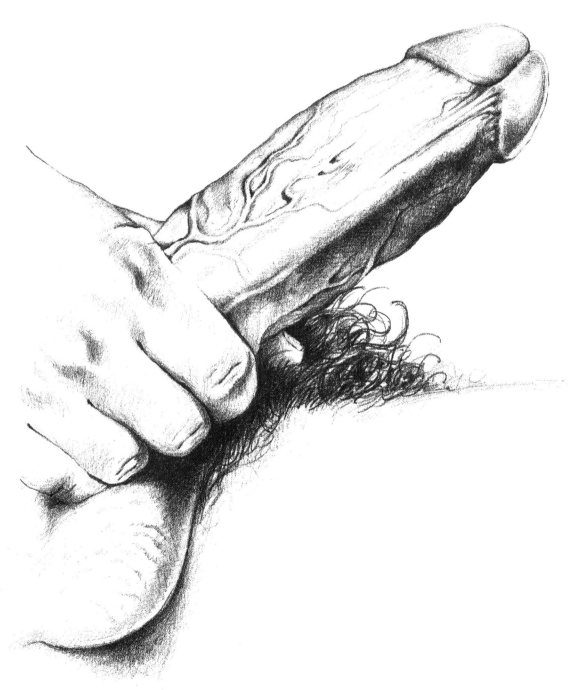

SEMEN. (The fluid produced during ejaculation, commonly referred to as *come* or *cum*.) Semen consists mainly of seminal fluid, produced by the prostate gland, and a small amount of sperm fluid from the testes. An average orgasm, for most men, produces about two teaspoons of semen. Want more? See the discussion under *Ejaculation*.

SEXUAL RESPONSE CYCLE. In their pioneering work *Human Sexual Response*, the sex research team of William Masters and Virginia Johnson defined four stages that both men and women experience during sex. Their description of this cycle provides a helpful overview, but it mustn't be taken as gospel. Some men, for example, report that the intense pleasure of orgasm begins well before they come, and has diminished by the time they ejaculate. Others continue to enjoy the sensation of pelvic thrusting, and may even feel the pleasure connected with orgasm, well after ejaculation. There are many ways to have an orgasm.

Excitement: As sexual stimulation begins, whether it's caused physically or is just in your mind, your heart rate and blood pressure increase. Blood pumps into your chest and nipples, ears, lips, genitals, and anus, increasing your sensitivity in these areas. You'll start to get an erection as blood engorges your penis; many men quickly get fully hard at this point. The skin of your scrotum thickens, and your testes are pulled up closer to your body. In some men, the nipples become erect.

Plateau: If the stimulation continues, your body steadily moves toward ejaculation and orgasm. Your penis will now be fully erect, and the head, filled with blood, is larger and has probably taken on a purplish hue. An occasional drop of pre-ejaculate may ooze from the tip. The prostate gland becomes larger and firmer; if your partner is fucking you, or using a finger to anally stimulate you, your prostate will grow more sensitive to these movements.

During this stage, your body tenses; perhaps you'll clench your buttocks and arch your back. Most men feel a natural inclination to thrust forward and back with their pelvis.

The anus may also contract during this period. This contraction can be more pleasurable when it takes place around another man's cock or finger.

With practice, you can learn to stop or cut down on stimulation during this period, so that you enjoy a high level of excitement for a longer period before you come.

Orgasm: At a certain point, you'll get the feeling of "ejaculatory inevitability." You know you're about to come, even without more stimulation. Your body has begun the internal contractions that will cause you to orgasm and ejaculate. Your muscles tense; your penis stiffens; areas such as your testicles and lips become even more sensitive. Sperm from your testes mixes in the urethra with fluid from other glands, creating semen. A few seconds later, muscles inside your body, at the base of your erect penis, will begin a series of rhythmic contractions, shooting out semen in several spurts.

Resolution: Soon after orgasm, the changes that began in the stimulation stage are reversed. Blood pressure drops, the penis becomes soft again, the nipples, lips, and ears lose their heightened sensitivity. Most men become relaxed during this stage. If it's nighttime, they'll roll over and fall sleep. For some couples, the openness created by the shared orgasm creates the right atmosphere for pillow talk.

A man who's uncomfortable with being gay, or with sex in general, may respond in quite the opposite way, becoming distant or even hostile toward the partner whom he now blames for having enticed him into something that he regrets.

Refractory period: Men, unlike women, also experience a refractory period following orgasm, during which they feel no interest in further sex, and can't get another erection. The penis may become so sensitive during this period that it's unpleasant for it to even be touched.

(See also *Genitals; Ejaculation; Erection; Orgasm; Refractory Period.*)

SEXUALLY TRANSMITTED DISEASE. (An illness commonly spread by sexual activity, also known as *STD, venereal disease,* or *VD.*)

Many sexually transmitted diseases (STD's) occur more often among gay men than in the general population. Several factors contribute to this difference: Gay men have the opportunity to engage in sex with more people than do most heterosexual men, and some practices common in the gay community — especially rimming and anal intercourse — are highly efficient ways of transmitting disease. In addition, closeted gay people often hesitate to get prompt medical attention for sexually transmitted diseases. Fortunately, the increasing acceptance of safer sex, as an AIDS-preventive measure, has also reduced the spread of other sexually transmitted diseases. The most common STD's are briefly discussed here. (See also *AIDS.*)

AMEBIASIS: Amebiasis is caused by a small parasite — an ameba — that lives in the large intestine. Until the 1970s, this ameba was little known in the United States. In recent years, however, it began to spread rapidly through sexual contact, and amebiasis is now recognized as a sexually transmitted disease.

Cause and Prevention. These amebas are usually passed through oral-anal contact. But they can be transmitted by any activity that allows one person's fecal matter to eventually come into contact with a partner's mouth. That means if you finger-fuck someone, then put your finger in your mouth without washing it, you can easily contract amebiasis.

Symptoms. It's possible to have amebiasis for years without showing any symptoms. However, once the amebas invade the actual wall of the bowel, symptoms usually appear. These may include a change in bowel habits; bloody diarrhea; and abdominal cramps.

Treatment. Amebiasis is difficult to diagnose. Usually several stool specimens are examined under a microscope for signs of infection; however, this method misses some cases. Nor is the treatment sure to be successful; none of the drugs available for amebiasis is always effective, and frequently two or three treatments are required.

CHLAMYDIA: Chlamydia is a family of organisms that cause several different diseases, including lymphogranuloma venereum (LGV) and nongonococcal urethritis (listed below as NGU/NSU).

Cause and Prevention. The various diseases associated with the chlamydia organisms are usually contracted sexually. The best means of prevention is to avoid contact with sexual partners who are infected. Condoms are protective.

Symptoms. Symptoms vary. Men usually experience burning on urination and a discharge from the penis. Many contagious people, both men and women, show no symptoms of the disease.

Treatment. Testing and treatment with antibiotics are necessary.

CRAB LICE: Known as "crabs," pubic lice are closely related to head and body lice, but they cannot infect the scalp, because they require hairs that are relatively far apart.

Cause and Prevention. Crabs, the most contagious STD, are usually caught from sexual partners. They can also spread through shared towels, clothing, or even toilet seats.

Symptoms. If you've got crabs, you'll feel an intense itching in the pubic area, starting three to four weeks after infection. The itching is frequently worse at night. Usually you can see the lice and their eggs (nits) in the pubic hair.

Treatment. The main prescription medication is gamma benzene hexachloride (sold under the name Kwell), which is available as a shampoo, cream, or lotion. The nits may have to be removed with a fine-tooth comb. Over-the-counter remedies are available, but they're not always effective.

GIARDIASIS: Giardiasis is similar to amebiasis, but is caused by a protozoan — *Giardia lamblia* — that lives in the small intestine. It's responsible for what is often known as "traveler's diarrhea," and in the past decade, has become common in gay men.

Cause and Prevention. The same anal-oral contact that transmits amebas will transmit giardia. However, it can be caught in many non-sexual ways as well, mostly from drinking contaminated water.

Symptoms. Diarrhea (without blood present), nausea, and cramps are among the most common symptoms. Sometimes there are no symptoms.

Treatment. Giardia, like amebas, is usually detected through a stool examination, although even then the disease is not always detectable. Several relatively effective drugs have been found for it.

GONORRHEA: Gonorrhea, known colloquially as the *clap,* the *drip,* or *GC,* is caused by bacteria that can infect the urethra, the rectum, the throat, or the eye. It can also appear as a generalized infection.

Cause and Prevention. Gonorrhea is usually caught through sexual contact with an infected partner, and the best prevention is to avoid having sex with someone who's got it. Urinating after sex may decrease the likelihood of developing it.

Symptoms. Symptoms vary, depending on which part of the body is infected. In men, the primary symptoms are a burning sensation when urinating, a penile discharge, and sometimes a sore throat or diarrhea. Anal gonorrhea may result in a discharge, but usually does not. Many people never develop symptoms, though they're still infected and contagious, especially when gonorrhea occurs in the throat or rectum. Likewise, vaginal infections in women often display no symptoms. Symptoms can first appear from one to thirty days after exposure; the average is three to five days.

Treatment. Patients must be treated with an appropriate antibiotic, depending on where the infection is located.

HEPATITIS-A: Hepatitis-A is caused by a virus that multiplies within the liver and inflames that organ. This is considered the least harmful type of hepatitis because it causes no permanent damage to the liver. A person who has had hepatitis-A will develop an immunity to future exposure, and will not be contagious after the initial bout is over.

Cause and Prevention. The hepatitis-A virus is found in fecal matter, and can be picked up by ingesting even a small amount of feces. Oral-anal sex is a common route of transmission, as is anal intercourse. (The use of a condom does not necessarily protect against this disease, since a man's hands may come into contact with fecal matter on the rubber while removing it, which can then be easily transmitted to the mouth.) Hepatitis-A is also sometimes caught from drinking contaminated water, from eating food that's not prepared under sanitary conditions, or from eating contaminated raw shellfish.

Symptoms. In its early stages, hepatitis-A often produces fever, headache, and loss of appetite. Then come the more distinctive symptoms: jaundice (a yellow tint to the eyes and skin); dark urine; and light, chalk-colored stools.

Treatment. Only in rare cases does hepatitis-A require hospitalization. Usually bed rest at home is adequate, and some people continue their daily routines while recovering from hepatitis-A. A person who suffers from hepatitis should not drink alcohol, as it will place a further burden on an already-strained liver. Drugs or medications should be used only after consulting with a doctor.

HEPATITIS-B: Like hepatitis-A, hepatitis-B is an inflammation of the liver. However, this variety is much more serious, sometimes causing permanent liver damage and cancer. Individuals infected with hepatitis-B may become permanent carriers, able to infect others for the rest of their lives. It is estimated that about five percent of gay men are chronic carriers.

Cause and Prevention. The hepatitis-B virus, like the AIDS virus, is carried in many bodily fluids, most notably blood and semen, and the two are transmitted similarly. Anal intercourse and needle-sharing are especially effective ways to transmit hepatitis-B. However, hepatitis-B is easier to transmit than HIV; you can become infected by sharing a toothbrush or drinking glass; during oral sex; or through any other activity that exposes you to the blood, semen, saliva, or urine of another person.

If you believe you've recently been infected with hepatitis-B, an inexpensive gamma globulin shot will fortify your body's short-term defenses against the disease. For the longer term, a hepatitis-B vaccine is now available. Although relatively expensive ($100 to $200), doctors recommend it for sexually active gay men who have not yet been infected. Many gay men are already immune.

Symptoms. About half of the people with hepatitis-B don't show any visible symptoms. When symptoms do appear, they may include fever or headache, aching joints, loss of appetite, or a rash. As with hepatitis-A, the best-known symptoms, which take slightly longer to appear, are jaundice (a yellow tint to the eyes and skin), dark urine, and light stools.

Treatment. Hepatitis-B is best diagnosed through blood tests. It usually does not require hospitalization, but adequate rest at home is important in fighting off the infection. Anyone still infected after about six months is considered to have chronic hepatitis.

HERPES SIMPLEX: The herpes simplex virus causes cold sores and genital infections. It belongs to a family of four DNA viruses that cannot be completely eradicated by the immune system. Once infection occurs, the virus remains in the body, even if no symptoms are present.

Cause and Prevention. Herpes is spread only through close physical contact involving the mucous membranes of the mouth, genitals, rectum, or eyes. As with other sexually transmitted diseases, the best prevention is to avoid sexual contact with infected persons. Although you can get herpes from asymptomatic partners, most people catch herpes from partners with visible lesions.

Symptoms. The primary symptom will be clusters of painful blisters or ulcers in the mouth or throat, on the penis, near or in the rectum, or on the buttocks. There may be itching or burning in the genital or rectal area. More general symptoms such as fever, headache, and vomiting may also be present.

Treatment. Acyclovir, an anti-viral drug, has been helpful in diminishing the severity and duration of outbreaks in some cases. However, it cannot prevent the virus from recurring unless it is taken daily.

NGU/NSU: Nongonococcal urethritis (NGU) or nonspecific urethritis (NSU) is an infection caused by any one of several bacteria-like organisms.

Cause and Prevention. NGU/NSU is usually transmitted through sexual contact.

Symptoms. Men will feel a burning sensation when urinating, and will have to urinate more often. A penile discharge often accompanies NGU. Because these symptoms are similar to those for gonorrhea — but will not respond to penicillin as gonorrhea usually does — neither you, nor your doctor, should assume that a penile discharge automatically indicates gonorrhea. The first symptoms appear after one to three weeks.

Treatment. NGU is usually treated with tetracycline. If NGU is accompanied by gonorrhea, additional drugs may be required.

SCABIES: Scabies is caused by a mite that's invisible to the naked eye. It belongs to the Arachnida class of insects, along with spiders and scorpions. Unlike pubic crabs, which stay on the surface of the skin, the female scabies mite burrows under the skin, where she lays her eggs.

Cause and Prevention. Scabies is transmitted primarily through close physical contact. Since the mite can survive on sheets and towels for two to three days, it's also possible to catch it from these items.

Symptoms. Itching begins about a month after infestation. It becomes especially severe at night.

Treatment. Like crabs, scabies is treated with Kwell. The cream or lotion must be applied to the entire body from the neck down, left on for eight to twenty-four hours, then washed off. A second application is necessary a week to ten days later to kill newly hatched organisms. Itching may persist for weeks, even after successful treatment.

SYPHILIS: Syphilis is caused by an organism known as a spirochete. In 1983, gay and bisexual men accounted for fifty percent of new cases. It's a serious disease which, if untreated, can many years later lead to brain damage, paralysis, heart disease, and death.

Cause and Prevention. The vast majority of syphilis cases are sexually transmitted. The spirochete enters the body through broken skin or mucous membranes. The best way to prevent syphilis is by avoiding sexual contact with infected partners, although the use of condoms and safer-sex practices will greatly reduce the likelihood of being infected.

Symptoms. The symptoms vary according to how long a person has been infected. The primary stage often produces a hard, red, painless bump at the point of contact, usually on the penile shaft or anus. This chancre will disappear after a few weeks — but you're still infected. In the secondary stage, a rash may develop, and lymph nodes may become swollen. A non-itchy rash, hair loss, and flu-like symptoms can also appear. Symptoms may appear ten to ninety days after exposure; the average period is three weeks.

Treatment. Syphilis must be treated with antibiotics, usually penicillin.

VENEREAL WARTS: Warts are skin tumors caused by a virus.

Cause and Prevention. Venereal warts are almost always sexually transmitted, and the only sure protection is to avoid any sexual contact with infected partners. Even the hand-to-genital contact of mutual masturbation can spread them. Once you're infected, warts can be "self-seeding" — that is, they can easily spread beyond the point of initial infection.

Symptoms. Warts usually grow around the anus, or on the shaft of the penis; on women, they'll appear around the vaginal opening. The warts themselves don't hurt, but they can lead to a secondary infection that makes them drain fluid, and may cause pain. They may make their first appearance several months after exposure. Anal warts can cause itching and bleeding during anal intercourse or after bowel movements.

Treatment. Several forms of treatment are possible. Podophyllin is the most common. It is applied directly to the warts and washed off several hours later. Other treatments include liquid nitrogen, lasers, and surgery. Repeated treatments are often necessary; if left untreated, genital warts may progress into cancer. You'll usually have to abstain from sex until your doctor tells you they're cured.

SHAVING. Some men enjoy the look of having part or all of their pubic hair shaved off.

Back in the days when physique models wore skimpy posing straps, to avoid obscenity prosecutions, they routinely shaved off any pubic hair that showed outside the strap. The combination of hairless inner thighs and a hairy chest looked odd, so they commonly shaved off their other body hair as well.

Today's porn stars often do the same, shaving most of the pubic area, leaving only the patch of hair above their cock. Some fashion-conscious gay men, always ready for something new, follow suit. A few go further, shaving off everything.

If you want to try it, all you'll need are common sense, a bit of caution, and a safety razor. It helps to soak in a warm bath first, then apply shaving cream and get started. Shaving chest and leg hair is no more difficult than shaving your face. If you shave your pubic hair, expect the skin to be sensitive and itchy for a few days, especially when you walk. This isn't something to try right before a long hike.

If you find that your pubic hair keeps getting caught in your condoms as you remove them, shaving your pubic hair is one way to alleviate the situation. Pubic shaving will also help get rid of a stubborn case of crabs, though usually less drastic measures will suffice.

SHOWING OFF. See *Exhibitionism.*

SIMULTANEOUS ORGASM. Somewhere, in some distant time, the notion took hold that perfect sex required that two people reach orgasm at the same time. It's no more true than the one about masturbation making hair grow on your palms.

Sometimes, such as during mutual masturbation, you'll both come simultaneously. Fine. That makes it harder to tell who missed the designated target and stained your new designer sheets. But many times, you'll want to both focus on one partner, then on the other.

Of the men who discussed their experiences for this book, there were several attitudes. "It depends what James and I are doing," said Jeff. "If we're jerking off, we usually get into some really deep kissing as we approach orgasm, and without even trying, we come together. We know each other pretty well by now. When we're doing something else — for example, I really like to lie on top of James as he makes a fist and I fuck it — then it's strictly one at a time. We finish one activity and one orgasm, and then move on to the other one. Of course, we try not to have too long a gap between them, or the person who came first starts to mellow out too much."

According to Ted, "Usually I'm fucking Andrew, and one of us is masturbating him at the same time. After so much time together, we know each other pretty well and tend to come within about thirty seconds of each other, but we don't make a big deal about it."

"I don't know that Jason and I have ever had simultaneous orgasms," said Phillip. "We focus on one person's orgasm at a time. If Jason comes first, which he usually does, sometimes he's ready to shoot again by the time I've climaxed."

If you do want to come together, don't expect it to happen by magic. Tell your partner how things are progressing: *I'm getting close ... I'm almost there ... I'm gonna come.* When you know each other well, the same communication can be achieved with moans that increase in frequency and intensity.

SIXTY-NINE. (Oral sex in which both partners suck the other's penis simultaneously.)

Sixty-nining sounds exciting and sexy. Unfortunately, it often loses something in practice. In most cases, the angles of your mouth and his cock won't be quite compatible: it's easier to scrape him with your teeth than when you're both facing the same way. Nor can your tongue reach the sensitive area just below the head of his cock.

Moreover, your attention is divided between two areas. You may find that you can't fully enjoy the sensation of your approaching orgasm, at the same time that you're trying to make him feel great.

But try it sometime anyway. Many men love this position, and most of us enjoy it on an occasional basis. Just because it's not right for everyone all the time doesn't mean it won't be right for you.

SLEEPING TOGETHER. A majority of couples say that sleeping together is an important part of their relationship. The bodily contact provides a welcome sense of security after a day in the real-world jungle.

But some people just don't sleep well with someone else in the bed. It may be simply that they're a light sleeper. Or perhaps they've got a bedmate who snores. If you're in this situation, and your partner clearly wants to be next to you every night, give it a fair try before you conclude that it's impossible. This may simply be a new habit that, once learned, you'll never want to give up.

If it really doesn't work, however, explain to your lover that it has nothing to do with your love for him, merely with your need to get a good night's sleep.

S/M. See *Sadomasochism.*

SPECIAL INTERESTS. It would be impossible to discuss all of the activities, physical traits, and objects that hold a special attraction for

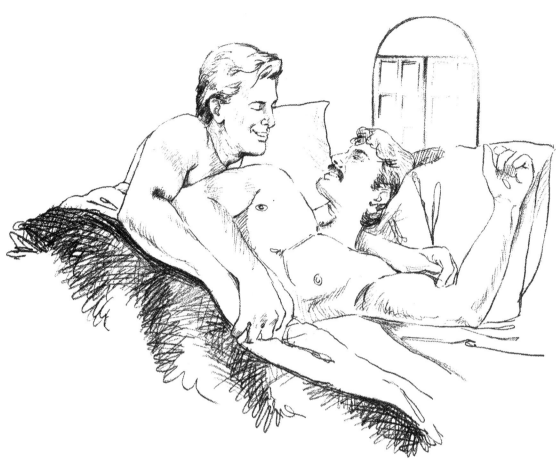

some gay men. The following very abbreviated list merely hints at the diversity to be found out there. In various magazines, books, and questionnaires, gay men have expressed strong erotic interest in:

- Amputees
- Being diapered
- Enemas
- Fat men
- Getting spanked
- Hairy chests
- Heterosexual porn
- Lesbians
- Men of another race or ethnic group
- Men older than 70
- Sex in a convertible
- Shaved genitals
- Small cocks
- Underwater sex
- Women's panties

And that, of course, doesn't even include the most widespread special interests: big cocks, Marines, watersports, and so on.

If you have an unusual sexual interest or attraction, you'll probably go through a process much like coming out. Originally you'll worry that you're the only man in the world turned on by, for example, diapers. Eventually you'll discover others who share your interest; if you're lucky, you'll tap into an entire underground network of fellow diaper devotees. As you meet others, you'll become more comfortable with your own identity. Still, just as many gay people remain closeted in selected situations, you may choose not to tell all your gay friends about your diaper fetish.

If your special interest involves an attraction to men because of a specific physical trait (including race) you may face another obstacle. Both you and your partner could worry that you're only attracted to him for that one characteristic. The fact is, *most* relationships start off with a physical attraction; if they last, it's because there was a good fit on other levels, as well.

Pat Califia, in her entertaining book *The Advocate Adviser*, gives a helpful perspective on such concerns. Responding to a 53-year-old double-amputee who has placed and answered several personal ads, but "all I've had are kinky replies," she writes:

"I know that you view your amputations as a misfortune. It isn't a fetish for you; it's made your life harder. But think about this. Would you rather have sex with someone who is doing you a favor, trying to overlook a handicap that they actually find upsetting, or would you rather have sex with someone who is attracted to you and finds that handicap exciting?

"Of course, you may eventually get lucky and meet someone who feels neutral about your disability because they are more interested in who you are as an individual than in your physical difference. That would be ideal. But in the meantime, why close yourself off?"

STRAIGHT MEN (AS SEX PARTNERS). A minority of gay men get turned on mainly by straight men. Some just like the challenge. For others, it's ego: "If I can get a straight man in bed with me, I must be really hot." Sometimes it's a way of avoiding emotional entanglements. And in a few sad cases, it's triggered by internalized homophobia: Sex with a straight man somehow doesn't seem quite as "gay," or a straight partner is seen as more masculine.

This is risky business. There's no simple way to tell which straight men will be open to your advances, which will politely rebuff you, and which will beat you up. And if you're fantasizing about a long-term relationship with one of these men, your head is way up in the clouds. Do some serious self-examination about just what your motives are, and whether those motives really bear pursuing.

STRANGULATION. Men who are executed by hanging get an erection as they die. At least, that's the rumor — it's hard to find clear documentation. Likewise, strangulation strengthens the sensation of orgasm — or so some people believe. Those who know best aren't talking.

These stories and speculations have encouraged some men to experiment with semi-strangulation as an adjutant to sex. Unfortunately, too many of them end up in the morgue. Usually they were masturbating alone and rigged up a way to create tension around their neck; when they lost consciousness, nobody was there to loosen the restraint. Deaths have also occurred, however, when two men just got carried away and common sense flew out the window.

Strangulation is one of those activities that just isn't worth the risk. There's no sense in letting the little death — *le petit mort,* as the French call an orgasm — become the big one.

Minimizing the risks: That said, there will still be those who want to try it. As with activities that may include a small risk of transmitting HIV, there's no clear agreement, among experts, on just how risky semi-strangulation has to be. Some feel there's no way to do it safely; others claim that with some simple precautions, this erotic diversion needn't carry a high risk. I'm not going to give instructions here; I merely want to suggest a couple of precautions that will minimize the risk.

First, if you have heart problems, or high or low blood pressure, talk to your doctor before trying anything that interferes with blood circulation. Second, do it with a partner — most fatal accidents involving strangulation occurred when someone was masturbating alone. Any mechanical device can fail. If you're with a partner, he can release it.

SURROGATE. (A sex partner who, working as a professional, helps a client deal with certain sexual dysfunctions.)

Surrogacy has been accepted for years as a legitimate way for straight men to deal with premature or retarded ejaculation, psychological impotence, and other dysfunctions that hinder their sex lives. Gay surrogacy is less common, but it seems likely to become more available in the years ahead.

When surrogates are appropriate: If you've already got a regular partner, most sexual difficulties are best resolved with that partner. You may ask a sex therapist to provide advice, but you're not likely to need a surrogate. The only exception is if your partner is so uncomfortable with sex that he can't provide the relaxed and unpressured setting that you may need.

Nor is a surrogate appropriate if you're really just looking for sex. Your sessions together won't provide what you have in mind.

It's called for in cases where you and your doctor agree that certain identifiable problems prevent you from enjoying sex as much as you could, and you have no other partner with whom to work through these problems.

Finding a surrogate: It's hard to find gay surrogates outside of the largest cities. Most of them work through a licensed therapist, and will only see clients who are in therapy. This protects them from being perceived as hustlers by the justice system, and it protects you from a surrogate whose eagerness for the job exceeds his qualifications. Expect to pay a surrogate about the same amount as you would any other health professional.

T

TEAROOM. (A public toilet used by gay men for quickie sex.)

Any medium-sized town has at least one public restroom where men meet to have sex. It's often at a bus terminal, or in a remote part of the college campus. In most tearooms, occupants will have a brief warning before someone entering can see what's going on.

The ritual varies little from city to city. A man stands at the urinal, fondling himself. Anyone interested stands at the adjacent urinal and does likewise. Once mutual interest has been established, the two can have sex right there, or may retire to the partial privacy of a stall.

In some cases, a man interested in sex indicates it simply by hanging around. By standing at the urinal, washing his hands, combing his hair, then returning to the urinal, he can stay in the restroom indefinitely without arousing the suspicion of heterosexuals who briefly stop in. Anyone who stays long enough to notice his peculiar activity is interested in the same thing — or else is a vice cop.

Contact can also take place between men in adjacent stalls. Usually it starts with foot shuffling or tapping, then one man slides his foot toward the other, who reciprocates. Communication may take the form of written notes passed back and forth.

You'll know you're in a tearoom for sure if you find a glory hole in the stall — a hole, at the appropriate level, large enough to accommodate an erect penis. Such holes provide an opportunity for the occupants to briefly size one another up, then proceed to some quick and anonymous sex.

Tearoom sex usually consists of mutual masturbation or sucking — it takes too long to stop fucking and get into a semi-plausible position, should you be interrupted. Men who go to tearooms for sex usually seek anonymity; often they're married men, and this is their only outlet for gay sex. They won't want to swap phone numbers afterward.

Hazards: Not surprisingly, local police and campus authorities aren't happy to have tearooms in their jurisdiction. Entrapment is still common in many areas. There's always the possibility that you're being observed, or even videotaped, from a concealed area. Police know that men arrested in tearooms will usually do anything to avoid further publicity — fines will be paid without a fuss, and police may even expect a "gratuity" for keeping things quiet. (See *Legal Trouble*.)

In addition to police, muggers find tearoom traffic to be easy pickings. A closeted man who drops his pants in a tearoom, then gets robbed, isn't likely to pursue his assailant or to go to the police.

TELEPHONE CRUISING. You're walking down the street. Suddenly the pay phone next to you rings. It couldn't possibly be for you, could it? After all, nobody knows you're there.

Actually, maybe it *is* for you. Men with apartments that overlook a pay phone sometimes call that number when they spot a man

walking toward it who appeals to them. In these situations, the caller is in control. He can see you, and evaluate you; you know nothing but the timbre of his voice. If you're adventuresome enough to pursue such an invitation, it's wise to have him meet you on the street, or at a coffee shop, before heading up to his apartment.

TELEPHONE SEX. (Masturbating while talking on the phone about sex.)

Phone sex enjoyed a small but avid following long before AIDS, but its popularity has soared in recent years as the ultimate in safe sex. It's most commonly used by men who are strangers to one another, but phone sex also allows monogamous couples to reach out and touch one another even when they're separated.

In the old days, phone sex meant that you'd call a number, and provide information so the fees could be charged to your credit card. You then received a live call-back, often tailored to your requests, and sometimes sounding quite bored.

Technology has changed all that. Commercial phone sex services now allow you to call a recorded message, or to hook in with one or several other callers for live action. You don't need a credit card; the charge will simply show up on your phone bill. That charge can be considerable: rates range from as little as ten cents a minute to as much as a dollar or two. Read the small print in the ad before you dial, and don't fall asleep while talking. One man who snoozed off ran up a $620 phone bill.

You can avoid the fees by joining a phone sex club, though it may be harder to find one. These are usually run as a hobby, on a non-commercial basis, so they have no money for advertising. Clubs have various operating procedures. Typically, members are listed along with special interests and the best times to call, and the listing is distributed only to other members. Then you're on your own.

The best place to find out about any of these services is a local or national gay publication.

TESTICLES. See *Genitals.*

THERAPY. All of us have difficulty, on occasion, dealing with the stresses and demands of daily life. Most of us have bouts with shyness, depression, and loneliness. Most of us have occasional sexual difficulties. If these are only occasional, it merely means you're a member of the human race. That doesn't call for therapy.

But if one of these conditions dominates your life and causes recurring problems, you need to break that pattern. The most obvious solution — and the most expensive — is private therapy. Other options are group therapy; self-help groups (including organizations like Alcoholics Anonymous); confiding in a friend; or checking your bookstore for books that address your concerns. With books, as with living therapists, you have to watch out for all the quacks out there, but at least they're less expensive quacks.

Beware of therapy if the cost will create more problems than it could possibly solve. In that case, check with your local or state health department to learn about programs that may help you.

Sex therapy: Therapy for a specific, continuing sexual problem is often worth the cost. In these cases, you'll have a specific goal, which makes it easier to evaluate your progress.

Couples therapy: Many relationships break up simply because the two people involved are so close to the problems that they can't see some obvious solutions. Just a few sessions of couples counseling can make a big difference. Even if you're breaking up, an experienced meditator can help negotiate the terms, and make your lives much simpler.

Finding a therapist: A therapist who's recommended by a trusted friend is better than one you find through any other source. Other options are to ask your doctor; look at the ads in your local gay paper; or call the nearest gay hotline.

None of these methods will insure getting a therapist who meets your needs. Have an initial consultation — some therapists will offer this free — before making a decision. During that consultation, you should be asking questions as well as answering them. A therapist who isn't openly gay should at least be gay-affirmative and knowledgeable about gay concerns. But most important, make sure you're comfortable with this person. The book *The Lavender Couch,* by Marny Hall, offers valuable advice for anyone who's contemplating therapy, or already in it.

THREE-WAYS. (Sex with three participants, also known as a ménage à trois.)

If the prospect of three-way sex intrigues you, you've probably already got ideas about what you'd like to all be doing together. Most activities that work for two can easily accommodate a third. A few merit special attention.

The classic three-way position involves a center man who's come to be known as Lucky Pierre. As one man fucks him from behind, he either fucks, or is sucked by, the third. This is a great fantasy that only occasionally works out smoothly in practice, and is best accomplished if you're all standing, or on your sides.

A three-person version of sixty-nine is possible, in which the first man sucks the second, who sucks the third, who sucks the first. This

172 ❖ THREE-WAYS.

is easiest if one man has his mouth in the back of his head instead of the front, but with a little experimentation, it can be managed anyway.

It's possible for one man to suck two cocks simultaneously, and if he's truly relaxed and experienced, to be fucked by two men at once. The positions involved will never be comfortable, and probably won't be as physically stimulating as two-way sex, but for a few men, the psychological thrill makes it all worthwhile.

Another option is for one man to watch, stroking himself, as the other two perform. You can all three take turns being the voyeur; this is the easiest three-way sex for non-gymnasts.

Interpersonal dynamics: Three-ways have great potential for making one person feel excluded. Pangs of jealousy and possessiveness that you thought you had overcome may surface midway through.

The best ménages à trois happen when a couple who are already secure with one another invite a third man to join them for an evening's frolic — provided the third man neither wants, nor expects, anything more. The couple can each devote most of their attention to the newcomer, without danger of slighting one another.

Likewise, if things have been rocky between you and your partner lately, inviting a third person to bed with you is *not* the best way to resolve everything.

It's perfectly possible, however, for three men who don't know one another to enjoy a ménage à trois. It will work best if each participant views it as an opportunity for an enjoyable evening, not as the start of a relationship with one of the other men. Avoid a situation in which you're eager to launch a lifelong relationship with one man, and aren't really interested in the other. If the potential exists for what you're after, then you can get him in a two-way. If it doesn't, your ambitions will just spoil the experience for everyone.

TOES. Toes are remarkably sensitive. Sucking or nibbling on just-washed, manicured toes can be a turn-on for both parties. For some men, the "just-washed" requirement can be skipped.

TRANSSEXUAL. (Someone who identifies as a member of the opposite sex. Transsexuals frequently feel that their birth gender is incorrect, and wish to take whatever steps are necessary to live as the gender they believe themselves to be.)

Transsexuality has a long history. Native Americans institution-alized a custom of *berdache*, in which an individual within the tribe was treated as a member of the opposite sex. These berdache were revered, and were often credited with magical powers. So far as historians can tell, berdache were usually homosexual, and were often transsexual.

Transsexuals in western culture have received far less support. Some have dealt with this prejudice by adopting a lifelong identity as a member of the opposite sex, sometimes even marrying, and not being found out until their death. Although transsexuals can be gay, straight, or bisexual, many of them ally with the gay community, which tends to be more tolerant of sexual diversity than does mainstream America.

Only within the last generation have transsexuals had the option of actually changing sex. In 1951, Christine Jorgensen became the first person to have undergone a sex-change operation. Today, surgeons regularly perform these operations on both men and women. Reputable surgeons, however, require that you take hormones and live as the opposite sex for a year before they'll perform surgery. (Some doctors will perform a radical mastectomy on a female-to-male transsexual without this wait, if it would be impractical for the individual to pass as a male without the surgery.)

TRANSVESTITE. (Someone who enjoys, or is sexually aroused by, dressing in clothing usually worn by the opposite sex. An individual who simply enjoys dressing in drag on occasion is not technically a transvestite; the label is more accurately applied to someone who feels a strong need to do so.)

Transvestites can be found in both the gay and straight communities, and face a good bit of prejudice from both. This is grossly unfair — transvestites have taken more than their share of the risks in the long struggle against homophobia.

The feminist movement, too, has given transvestites a hard time, claiming that the desire to dress or look like a woman is somehow a remnant of a sexist society. But it's not that simple. Some transvestites try to pass as women. Others are merely refusing to conform to the standards of male behavior that society imposes. As their true personality comes out, they may freely mix the dress and roles expected of each gender. The result is disconcerting to many people, but ultimately, society needs this kind of shaking-up if it's ever to provide its members with more leeway to be ourselves.

TROILISM. (Becoming excited by watching one's lover engage in sex with another person.) See *Voyeurism, Three-Ways.*

TYPES. "He's just my type." "I liked him, but he wasn't my type." Such comments are common as gay men talk about their sex lives and loves.

All of us seem to have a certain type — a look that we find to be the ultimate in physical beauty. For one man, it's the slim, blond, bronzed young surfer. For another, it's the Marlboro Man. Others have more unusual tastes — there are chubby chasers, and men who are attracted to amputees, and those who just can't get it up unless their partner is bald.

There's nothing unusual about such preferences, and certainly nothing wrong with them. If you're lucky, you'll find a man who is as turned on by your physical traits as you are by his, then you'll discover that you share other interests, and you'll walk off into the sunset together.

However, it's possible to put too much emphasis on types. If you're unsatisfied with your love life, ask yourself whether you're limiting the field unrealistically. Are you ruling out relationships with men who aren't precisely your type, but who you like and who, if things developed, you could readily find attractive? Someone who doesn't stand out as you quickly scan the bar might be far more attractive after a quiet candlelight dinner together.

Just as you have your preferred types, so do other men. You'll save yourself much unhappiness in life by accepting the fact that some men will find you to be their type, and others won't.

Another pitfall awaits those who worry that their lover is *only* interested in them because they're his type. The well-endowed man who's involved with a size queen worries that "he only likes me for my cock." The handsome weight lifter worries that "they aren't really interested in the inner me." The concern may be even stronger for men who typify a characteristic that's socially devalued — being older, or an amputee, for example.

Such fears are really just that old nemesis, the inferiority complex, raising its head in a new form. You're taking a wonderful, positive fact — your lover gets turned on by you — and looking for a down-side to it. Don't let your mind play those games with you. Whatever physical trait attracts your partner, other men out there had the same traits. But he chose you. What's to complain about?

U-Z

VACUUM PUMP. (A gadget that claims to increase penis size by creating a vacuum around the penis.)

A number of vacuum-based penis enlargers are on the market. Most of them work as long as your penis is in the tube, and even briefly thereafter. They don't create any lasting change. (Unless you apply too much pressure, in which case they can damage your penis and reduce your ability to get erections.) As long as you don't expect them to perform miracles, these pumps can be a lot of fun for both solo sex, or exhibitionism with a partner.

Unfortunately, advertising for vacuum pumps has given some men the idea of saving money by using a vacuum cleaner for the same purpose. Many common household items can be integrated into sex play. Vacuum cleaners are not one of them.

A number of injuries have been caused by vacuum cleaners. The most common are simply cuts and bruises that occurred when the vacuum turned out to be more powerful than anticipated. More serious is the story of the man who disconnected the hose and stuck his cock directly into the vacuum cleaner opening, only to have it sucked into the fan inside. This may simply be another bit of American folklore, like the woman who put her poodle in the microwave to dry it out, but it vividly underscores the importance of never setting aside your common sense.

VENEREAL DISEASE. See *Sexually Transmitted Disease.*

VIBRATOR. (A hand-held electrical device that vibrates rapidly, used for sexual stimulation.)

Women have known for years about the magic that a well-placed vibrator can perform. Some are shaped like a dildo and can be used anally (see *Dildo*). A less common variation, known as a come cup, fits over the head of the penis. When it's turned on, it can trigger an orgasm with remarkable speed.

A vibrator of any shape can simply be held directly against the shaft of the penis or the balls for a type of pleasure that just can't be achieved any other way. Some guys like the feeling of putting a piece of cloth or fur between the vibrator and their skin.

VOYEURISM. (Erotic arousal caused by watching another person undress or engage in sex. Often the term implies that the person being watched is unaware of the watcher.)

Gay men are quite receptive to visual stimulation, as evidenced by the wide availability of porn magazines and videos. These are fine; the models and actors all knew the score, and they're happy to perform.

The ethical and legal issues arise when you're watching someone unawares. If you live in a gay neighborhood, and the hunk across the street enjoys lying down in front of the window and jerking off with all the lights on, it's a pretty good bet that while he may not know you're watching, he hopes you are. Enjoy the show, and hope that the landlord doesn't find out and raise your rent. But when you start climbing trees or fire escapes, or otherwise make a special effort to watch someone who has a reasonable expectation of privacy, you're breaking the law. Find a consenting partner who shares your fantasies.

Most of us probably have a touch of both the voyeur and the exhibitionist in us, and it's easy to indulge those tastes with a partner. Mutual masturbation involves an element of both. You can seductively undress in front of each other, if that makes things more enjoyable. Some couples go even farther: one gets in a position where he can't be seen, and watches as the other slowly leafs through some porn, strips off his clothes, and jerks off. Or find another couple who share your voyeuristic tendencies. You'll not only get turned on by watching one another; you'll probably learn some new techniques, as well.

On a grander scale, many cities now have jerk-off clubs, where show-and-tell is not just accepted, it's the rule. (See also *Exhibitionism; J/O Clubs; J/O Parties.*)

WATERSPORTS. (Sexual activity involving urine, also known as *golden showers.*)

Watersports usually involves urinating on one another; or drinking another man's urine, usually as it arcs out directly from the source. It's preceded by a good bit of liquid intake. Beer is the beverage of choice: it fills the bladder quickly, loosens inhibitions, and produces a bland urine. (Avoid asparagus that day; it has the opposite effect on taste.)

Safety: There's no danger in letting urine come into contact with unbroken skin. Watersports usually occur in the bathtub, and are followed by a more conventional shower. This is a minority interest, but if it appeals to you and your partner, there's no reason to hold back.

Drinking another man's urine carries more potential danger, though most men who do so suffer no ill effects. Some authorities believe there's a small theoretical danger of transmitting AIDS this way; others, including former U.S. Surgeon General C. Everett Koop, say there is not. A greater risk is that you'll transmit hepatitis, which can be carried by an apparently healthy man. Avoid letting urine come into contact with the eyes; if your partner has gonorrhea, it can cause blindness.

WRESTLING. For some reason, certain fantasies are especially prevalent among gay men. Wrestling is one such fantasy — and an easy one to turn into reality.

Wrestling, whether in the buff or while wearing a jockstrap or lycra tights, forces you to drop your inhibitions and get plenty of skin-to-skin contact with another man. You'll feel your partner's muscles tense and watch his buttocks clench. Then there's the moment of victory, as one of you kneels over the other, triumphant, yet exposed...

After a good bout of wrestling with a man who really turns you on, you're sure to end up sweaty and achingly hard. Some couples add

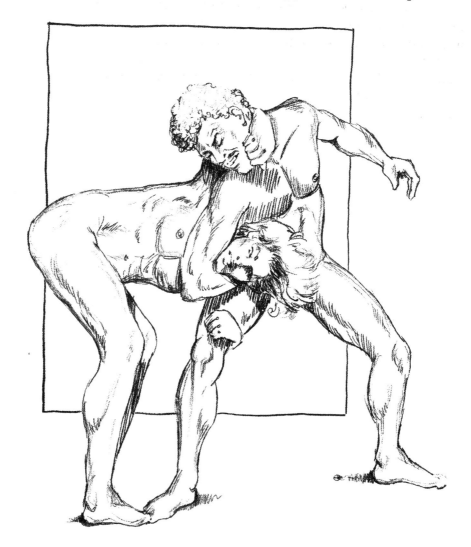

an extra twist to the fun, by agreeing in advance that the victor will call the shots in the sex play that follows.

ZOOPHILIA. (Sex with animals, also known as *bestiality.*)

City slickers tend to view the subject as a matter for jokes, but for boys growing up on a farm, sex with animals is not uncommon.

Thirteen percent of respondents to the 1977 *Gay Report* said they had tried sex with an animal at least once. "Living on a farm can be lovely," wrote one. "I've fucked many cows and had calves suck me off." In urban environments, zoophilia, when it occurs, is more likely to involve large dogs.

Zoophilia raises some ethical questions. Presumably the Animal Liberation Front wouldn't approve of sex with any animal that couldn't voice its consent. Still, it's hard to follow the mainstream logic that says it's okay for a cow to become your dinner, but not your lover. You're on your own in these largely uncharted waters.

But do use some sense so as not to run aground. Don't try to penetrate an animal that can't accommodate you; you'll cause pain and injury. For the same reasons, don't let yourself be penetrated by an animal — a stallion or bull, for example — that's bigger or stronger than you. AIDS apparently cannot be passed from an animal to a human, but other diseases can be; you're well advised to wear a rubber. The simplest way to enjoy bestiality is to keep it a fantasy.

When I agreed to write this book, the publisher offered to help by supplying several items, including a chart that would show the comparative risk of various sexual activities. Little did he suspect what a difficult job that would be!

As it turned out, no such chart existed. The Centers for Disease Control didn't have one. Neither did the major national AIDS organizations. Nor had anyone even compiled the data that would be needed to create it. As we made inquiries, several AIDS educators said they would love to see such a chart, while at least two protested that it was a bad idea. Any attempt to quantify these risks, they argued, would encourage individuals to engage in low-risk activities rather than sticking only to risk-free sex.

Obviously, both the publisher and I disagree, or we wouldn't have created a chart and included it in this book. (It appears under *Risk reduction,* and is also reproduced on the facing page.) I feel it is helpful for individuals making decisions about sex to graphically see the differences in perceived risks.

Moreover, the dividing line between "low-risk" and "risk-free" is not that clear. Mutual masturbation is on everybody's list of "safe" activities. Yet two of our ten respondents felt that "mutual masturbation — semen not touching one another" involved a slight risk! (They both gave it a rating of five on a scae of zero to one thousand — the others all rated it zero.) Half our respondents felt that you could perform oral sex on a man who was wearing a condom, to the point of ejaculation, without any risk; the other half gave this activity a rating of 10 to 50.

Rarely is it a good policy to withhold information from the public on the grounds that people won't use it wisely. Even when that information consists of compiled opinion, not scientific fact, it's still far more useful than the hunches that most individuals must currently rely on.

In addition, this chart highlights some issues that AIDS services need to address. There were startling discrepancies in the opinions we received. Our survey was answered by ten professional AIDS

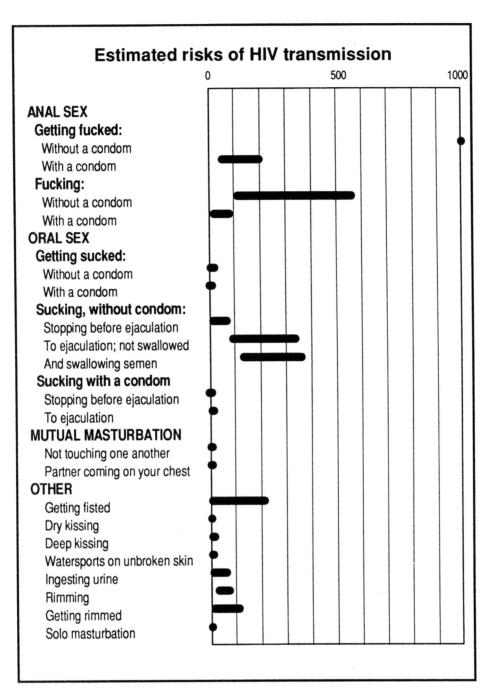

Estimated risks of HIV transmission

ANAL SEX
  Getting fucked:
    Without a condom
    With a condom
  Fucking:
    Without a condom
    With a condom
ORAL SEX
  Getting sucked:
    Without a condom
    With a condom
  Sucking, without condom:
    Stopping before ejaculation
    To ejaculation; not swallowed
    And swallowing semen
  Sucking with a condom
    Stopping before ejaculation
    To ejaculation
MUTUAL MASTURBATION
    Not touching one another
    Partner coming on your chest
OTHER
    Getting fisted
    Dry kissing
    Deep kissing
    Watersports on unbroken skin
    Ingesting urine
    Rimming
    Getting rimmed
    Solo masturbation

educators. Three of them said that getting fisted involved absolutely no risk of HIV infection — they rated this activity zero. Yet three gave it a rating of 300, suggesting that it carried a very high risk.

A discrepancy that large isn't merely based on different interpretations of the same medical data. Somewhere, the facts aren't getting through. Medical evidence suggests that the risk of HIV transmission through being fisted is very low. Perhaps respondents who gave a high response were either reacting to personal prejudice against fisting, or wanted to warn people away from it because of other health hazards involved, even though our survey asked them to address just the risk of HIV infection.

We hope that seeing this graph will encourage individuals to discuss these issues with their sex partners. In addition, we hope it will help health professionals to pinpoint the areas where existing information has not been disseminated well enough, and where more research is needed.

Using it: This chart should be used in combination with the background and advice in the *Risk reduction* section. Only the likelihood of HIV transmission is evaluated here. Some practices — most notably rimming and getting fisted — involve other health hazards, which must also be taken into account.

Method of survey: Since the publication of this chart may be controversial, it seems appropriate to provide some detail about just how it was prepared. We sent a one-page survey to several dozen AIDS educators around the country. We listed a number of activities, and to establish a scale, we defined receptive anal intercourse, without a condom, as having a high risk (rating 1000) and solo masturbation as being risk-free (rating 0). We asked them to rate other activities on this scale.

Ten individuals returned the survey. While this would be too small a sampling for a scientific analysis, we found it adequate for the purposes of this chart. For each activity, we analyzed the responses as follows:

If the lowest rating it received from anyone was less than half the next lowest rating, we threw that number out before compiling the results. Likewise, if the highest rating was more than double the next highest rating, we threw it out. This prevented the data from being skewed by a single respondent who may have misunderstood the question, or used outdated information.

We then arranged the answers in numerical order. We averaged the lowest half of them, then the highest half, and used those two averages to determine the low and high ends of the bar for that activity on the chart.

It is not possible with these bars graph to see precisely where a bar starts and ends. We chose not to give those numbers. This underscores the fact that the graph illustrates a consensus of opinions, not hard medical fact. The general trends and relationships shown here are significant and, we believe, helpful. The precise numbers would not be.

ANNOTATED BIBLIOGRAPHY

The Advocate. Published biweekly by Liberation Publications, P.O. Box 4371, Los Angeles, Calif. 90099.

Everybody complains about *The Advocate,* but nobody has produced a magazine or newspaper that gives better overall coverage of the gay community nationwide. If you're a sexually active gay man, you need to stay up to date on AIDS and other issues that vitally affect you. (Locally-based publications with national circulation, such as *Gay Community News,* and the *New York Native* make for provocative reading, but the publishers of each have such strong biases about AIDS and gay politics than they aren't good overall sources of information, especially about AIDS.)

The Advocate Adviser, by Pat Califia. Boston: Alyson Publications, 1991.

For a decade, Pat Califia has been answering questions that readers mail to her at The Advocate, with a refreshing blend of blunt honesty and humor. She covers every subject (as the book cover says) "from the ethics of zoophilia to the etiquette of a holy union ceremony, from interracial relationships to in-law problems." Much of her advice deals with sexual issues and differences.

The Alyson Almanac. Boston: Alyson Publications, 1990.

Here you'll find a wide range of information about gay history and culture, and specific entries about bookstores, newspapers, and hotline phone numbers in major cities, plus listings for major national organizations and publications.

American Couples, by Philip Blumstein and Pepper Schwartz. New York: William Morrow and Co., 1983.

When the authors undertook this major study of couples, they used three categories: married heterosexuals; unmarried heterosexual couples; and gay or lesbian couples. It was one of the few times that gay people have been included, on equal footing, in such a far-reaching study. The authors found intriguing similarities, and occasionally dramatic differences, when they compared the ways that different couples respond to the stresses of work, sex, and money.

Anal Pleasure and Health: A guide for men and women, by Jack Morin. Burlingame, Calif.: Yes Press, rev. 1986.

Morin sheds quite a bit of light on a little-discussed subject. He explains the origins of the anal taboo, and ways to safely and enjoyable explore anal sex play.

Coming Out Right: A handbook for the gay male, by Wes Muchmore and William Hanson. Boston: Alyson Publications, revised 1991.

Men of any age who are just coming out will find this to be a useful introduction to many facets of gay life.

The Complete Guide to Safe Sex, by the Institute for Advance Study of Human Sexuality. Beverly Hills: Specific Press, 1987.

A factual, detailed, and highly readable guide. Do you find most condoms too large or too small? This book lists popular brands with lengths and widths.

The Encyclopedia of Homosexuality, edited by Wayne R. Dynes. New York and London: Garland Publishing, 1990.

This comprehensive two-volume work presents a detailed look at a wide spectrum of subjects. The emphasis is on history, biography, and politics rather than how-to-do-it sex information, but any gay man could spend many hours happily browsing in this. Unfortunately, with its $150 price tag, that browsing will probably have to take place in a library.

The Gay Report, by Karla Jay and Allen Young. New York: Summit Books, 1977.

Five thousand gay men and lesbians filled out extensive questionnaires about their lifestyles and sexual experiences, which the authors tabulated for this 800-page book. They did not use scientific sampling techniques, and the survey was conducted in the pre-AIDS era, so their extensive statistical tables don't necessarily reflect today's realities — but they're interesting, nonetheless. (Some of the estimates in *Gay Sex* about the approximate frequency of various sexual acts are however derived from *The Gay Report,* since it's the best available source of actual numbers.) The authors have also included comments from many respondents that are, in turn, informative, entertaining, and erotic.

Gayellow Pages. New York: Renaissance House, revised annually.

The best single source of information about gay organizations and businesses throughout the U.S. and Canada. Arranged by city, here are listings for hotlines (which you can call for all sorts of information), bars, restaurants, bookstores, religious groups, social organizations, and more. An updated edition is published each year; this sort of information changes frequently, so be sure you get the most recent edition.

Getting Sex, by John Alan Lee. Don Mills, Ontario: Musson Book Co., 1978.

Entertaining, no-nonsense guide for gay men looking for casual sex.

How to Persuade Your Lover to Use a Condom ... And Why You Should, by Patti Breitman, Kim Knutson, and Paul Reed. Rockland, Calif.: Prima Publishing, 1987.

A very short book with suggestions that will be helpful if you're having difficulty in the area suggested by the title.

The Joy of Gay Sex, by Charles Silverstein and Edmund White. New York: Crown Publishers, 1977.

A lively and popular coffee-table book when it was first published, *The Joy of Gay Sex* is now long out of print and very out of date.

The Joy of Sex; More Joy of Sex, by Alex Comfort. New York: Simon and Schuster, revised 1987.

What a shame that a book that could so easily have spoken to all sexual orientations should be so rigidly heterosexual! The new revised edition has been "updated" with material about AIDS which is so simplistic that the book is not merely useless for gay men, it's downright offensive.

The Lavender Couch, by Marny Hall. Boston: Alyson Publications,

Clear, practical advice about how to decide whether to get into therapy; choosing among the various types of therapy that are available; finding a good therapist; and how to be sure you're getting what you need from it.

The Leatherman's Handbook II, by Larry Townsend. New York: Carlyle Communications, revised 1989.

First published in 1983, Townsend's book quickly became a bible for the S/M community. Both novices and experienced leathermen will welcome the hot fantasies in this new edition.

A Legal Guide for Lesbian and Gay Couples, by Hayden Curry and Denis Clifford. Berkeley: Nolo Press, rev. 1988.

Gay relationships do not automatically get the same legal rights that heterosexual marriages do. But certain simple steps can protect your rights and your relationship, and avoid problems if you break up, or if one partner dies or becomes incapacitated. If you're in a serious relationship, especially one that involves shared property or child custody, this book is a good investment.

The Lesbian S/M Safety Manual, edited by Pat Califia. Boston: Alyson Publications, 1988.

Ignore the title: Most of the information in this succinct guide will also be useful for men who are into S/M.

Male Sexuality, by Bernie Zilbergeld. New York: Bantam Books, 1978.

For a good overview of male sexuality, this is the best book available. Although writing primarily for the heterosexual male, Zilbergeld shows none of the discomfort with homosexuality that so many other non-gay writers exhibit. In contrast to *The Joy of Sex,* this book has a great deal of information that will be useful to gay men, including several chapters about ejaculatory control and erection problems, and numerous exercises to help the reader explore aspects of his sexuality.

Men Loving Men: A gay sex guide and consciousness book, by Mitch Walker. San Francisco: Gay Sunshine Press, 1977, 1985.

Walker brings a strong sense of other cultures and eras, and a warm spirituality, to his candid discussion of sex. Unfortunately, the book was written prior to the AIDS epidemic, and a chapter about health tacked onto the end is not adequate to bring the book up to date.

Sexual Happiness for Men: A practical approach, by Maurice Yaffe and Elizabeth Fenwick. New York: Henry Holt, 1988.

Although their book is directed at heterosexual men, the authors' insights (and especially their advice about erection and ejaculatory problems) will be helpful for gay men, as well.

Society and the Healthy Homosexual, by George Weinberg. New York: St. Martin's Press, 1972.

In this classic work, Weinberg first introduced the concept of homophobia. Although the book is now two decades old, it's still a wonderful source of insight and support for anyone who's still coming to terms with being gay.

Solo Sex: Advanced techniques, by Dr. Harold Litten. Mobile: Factor Press, 1990.

Here's an entire book about masturbation, with chapters devoted to toys, techniques, and fantasies — and it's very gay-positive. It's published by a small press and won't be widely available; if your nearest gay bookstore doesn't stock it, ask them to order it.

INDEX

Other books of interest from
ALYSON PUBLICATIONS

COMING OUT RIGHT, by Wes Muchmore and William Hanson, $8.00. A practical guide for the newly-out gay man revised for the realities of the 1990s.

THE ADVOCATE ADVISER, by Pat Califia, $9.00. Advice that Miss Manners would never have *dreamed* of giving.

THE ALYSON ALMANAC, by , $9.00. History, biographies, a congressional report card, and scores of useful addresses are collected here.

THE GAY BOOK OF LISTS, by Leigh Rutledge, $8.00. A fascinating compilation of gay history, personalities, and trivia.

LAVENDER LISTS, by Lynne Y. Fletcher and Adrien Saks, $9.00. Dozens of clever and original lists give the reader interesting and entertaining snippets of gay and lesbian lore.

BROTHER TO BROTHER, edited by Essex Hemphill, $9.00. Fiction, essays, and poetry by black gay men.

BI ANY OTHER NAME, edited by Loraine Hutchins and Lani Kaahumanu, $12.00. Hear the voices of over seventy women and men from all walks of life describe their lives as bisexuals.

- -

Most of these books are available at your nearest good bookstore. If you can't get these books locally, order by mail using this form.

Enclosed is $_____ for the following books. (Add $1.00 postage when ordering just one book. If you order two or more, we'll pay the postage.)

1. _____

2. _____

3. _____

name:_____ address:_____

city: _____ state: _____ zip: _____

ALYSON PUBLICATIONS
Dept. H-70, 40 Plympton St., Boston, MA 02118
After December 31, 1992, please write for current catalog.